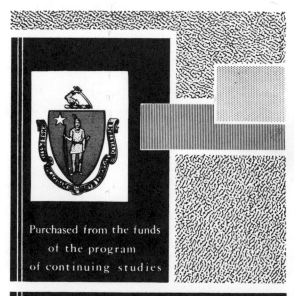

# MASSACHUSETTS
# STATE COLLEGE

### At

### FRAMINGHAM

# Protozoan Nutrition

*Protozoan Nutrition*
is one of a special series
of brief books
covering selected
topics in the pure
and applied sciences.

Paul R. Gross
*Brown University*

CONSULTING EDITOR

# Protozoan Nutrition

R. P. HALL

*New York University*

BLAISDELL PUBLISHING COMPANY

*A Division of Ginn and Company*

NEW YORK · LONDON · TORONTO

FIRST EDITION, 1965

2/66

# Contents

*Protozoan Nutrition*

# 1. Introduction

Protozoan nutrition, so far as the Protozoa themselves are concerned, involves two general problems: (1) finding the necessary foods, which is usually a matter of chance; and (2) getting such foods inside the body for use in metabolism. Free-living species find their food supply in the medium surrounding them. Parasitic species depend upon the body fluids or tissue cells of the host, upon intestinal microorganisms, or upon non-living materials ingested by the host.

The sources and relative abundance of food naturally are important factors influencing the survival and ecological distribution of Protozoa. Ecological niches may vary both with respect to the quantity of available food and, more specifically, with respect to the quantity of particular materials needed in a protozoan diet. In some natural waters, low in both organic and mineral content, Protozoa lead a rather precarious existence, barely escaping starvation, managing to survive only as sparse populations. In such environments, slight changes in concentration of a few elements, even a single element or one vitamin, might lead to a greater density or to the practical disappearance of a susceptible population. With higher concentrations of food, the margin between success and failure becomes wider, subject to interspecific competition. Larger populations may survive under normal conditions. However, increases

1

in food beyond certain levels may tend to limit an ecological niche to groups of organisms which can tolerate rather high concentrations of such materials or their metabolic products.

Students of protozoan ecology are currently interested in such nutritional problems as the identification of essential foods and vitamins for a variety of species and the distribution of such materials in natural environments. The investigation of these problems goes beyond fundamental research, of academic interest primarily, into such practical matters as factors influencing productivity of the lakes and oceans and potential methods for stabilizing or increasing the yield of natural waters. Some optimists believe that protozoologists may eventually find themselves allied with "farmers of the sea" in mutually advantageous endeavors. However, it should be realized that much of the ocean is not highly productive. In terms of actual organic nutrients, Ryther has estimated that a pound of fresh beans is equivalent to about 5,000,000 gallons of water from the open ocean.

Contributions of protozoologists to the investigation of nutritional problems must be based primarily on laboratory investigations, for it is only in pure (axenic) cultures of Protozoa in chemically defined media that their basal food requirements can be determined accurately. Even these techniques leave some problems unsettled. The definitive nature of a protozoologist's conclusions may be limited occasionally by the scarcity of adequately purified chemicals. For example, the absolute need for a particular metal might remain somewhat uncertain because it is difficult or even impossible in practice to prepare a control medium free from the metal under consideration. Similar difficulties have been encountered in pinning down an apparent need for a particular organic growth-factor.

The nutrition of parasitic Protozoa, in addition to the interest stemming from possibly unusual requirements, is potentially of practical importance because adequate knowledge may indicate points at which particular parasites are probably vulnerable to chemotherapeutic attack. A case in point is the development of Daraprim, an antifolic drug which is very effective against malarial parasites. Laboratory investigations in this area of protozoan nutrition have been handicapped somewhat by the sheer complexity of the food requirements for many parasites and the consequent problems in developing adequately defined media. Even after discovery of what seems to be a very effective drug, the host must be much less susceptible than the parasite if the new drug is to have real chemotherapeutic value.

The steady accumulation of pertinent data makes it increasingly clear that there is still much to be learned about specific food requirements in the different groups of Protozoa. There is also not enough basic information concerning the mechanisms by which food from the surrounding medium gets into the body of a protozoon. The conventional terms, *phagotrophic* (or holozoic) and *saprozoic* (or osmotrophic), differentiate ingestion of visible particles from the uptake of materials in solution. However, a phagotrophic organism is rarely, if ever, restricted entirely to the ingestion of solid food. Typically, such a phagotroph obtains some of its food by saprozoic methods and, under experimental conditions, it has been possible to grow certain normally phagotrophic species in completely soluble non-particulate media. Certain of the chlorophyll-bearing flagellates (e.g., *Ochromonas* and related genera) combine both phagotrophic and saprozoic nutrition with the ability to carry on photosynthesis. Mechanisms involved in phagotrophic and saprozoic feeding and the factors influencing such feeding need further investigation.

# 2. How Protozoa Obtain Food

## Phagotrophic (or Holozoic) Nutrition

Phagotrophy, or the habit of eating solid food, has been considered a prime factor in the divergence of animals and plants in evolution (Sandon, 1932). According to this view, the need to capture and ingest food was a major selective influence in evolution of locomotor organelles and complex responses to stimuli which generally characterize animals rather than plants. Phagotrophy, now that animals have this ability as a rule, affords certain advantages to a protozoon. So long as an environment can support some green algae and flagellates, it might be expected to maintain at least a small population of herbivorous phagotrophs. This puts a rather low limit on the concentration of dissolved organic food permitting survival of such phagotrophs. An environment with only a little food in solution would not necessarily be barred to phagotrophs because they have become adapted to eating concentrated packages of food. The primary tasks, uptake and concentration of raw materials and synthesis of protoplasm, have already been completed by microorganisms representing the food supply of the phagotrophs. Even carnivores, by preying upon the herbivores, might be able to survive in small numbers, although they would find the hunting tedious in an environment suitable primarily for sparse populations of photosynthetic types. More favorable environments, with higher concentrations of basal foods can support heavier populations of algae, green flagellates and bacteria — thus more food for herbivores, and in turn more food for carnivores.

The nutritional value of phagotrophy has not been evaluated very precisely by laboratory investigations so far. However, calculations (Seaman, 1961) based on several types of data indicate that, in pure cultures maintained in completely soluble media, less than 10 per cent of the food utilized by *Tetrahymena pyriformis*, a small ciliate, actually enters the body by ingestion. In fact, in a chemically defined medium very few food vacuoles are formed unless some inducing substance, such as a peptone, is added to the culture medium. Such data might imply that phagocytosis normally contributes little to the survival of this ciliate. However, Johnson (1936) maintained a strain of *T. pyriformis* in sterile salt solution to which had been added a killed suspension of washed bacteria (*Aerobacter aerogenes*, or any other of three additional species tested). Under these conditions, the ciliates were forced to depend primarily upon ingested bacteria instead of dissolved organic materials. Phagocytosis obviously was important in this case. Although a medium containing microorganisms would seem to be a more natural one than an axenic medium containing dissolved materials only, the relative importance of phagotrophy apparently depends to some extent upon the nature of the available food supply and possibly other factors in the environment. However, the survival of mouthless parasitic ciliates (Order Astomatida, for example) shows that at least some of the ciliates can thrive without ingestion of solid food. The mere existence of such organisms encourages the suspicion that in a favorable medium the average ciliate, even though naturally phagotrophic, may be able to take in much or even all of its needed food directly through the body wall.

## PHAGOTROPHY IN SARCODINA

One of the unexpected findings on amoebae is that at least certain species have a fairly definite "working day." Thus: "At dawn, only Brownian movements occur in the cytoplasm. Activity of cytoplasm and frequent changes of shape occur in early morning hours; slow to moderate locomotion and feeding until about noon; rapid locomotion with occasional halts and continuance to about 3:00 P.M.; regression of activity and locomotion until about dusk; cessation of movement within an hour after dusk" (Bovee, 1956). Although it may be tempting to suspect some sort of conformity to "union work rules" based on daily environmental changes, the observed sequence also might be related to the growth cycle of the organism.

The mechanical aspects of phagotrophy vary somewhat with the species. So far as visible activities go, amoeboid organisms have solved their problem of ingestion in several different ways. In many amoebae a fairly large morsel, such as a ciliate, may be surrounded by pseudopodia extended for the purpose and so enclosed in a food cup which becomes a *food vacuole*, the lining of which seems to be derived from the surface layer of the organism or at least the plasma membrane. Such food-cups (Figures 1, 2) as described in *Amoeba proteus* (Mast and Root, 1916) and *Pelomyxa carolinensis* (Kudo, 1946), are capable of cutting or tearing partially ingested prey into pieces. The mechanism apparently differs in these two organisms. In *A. proteus*, the reported observations suggest a substantial pressure by the edge of the food-cup; in other words, the amoeba seems to bite the ciliate in two. *Pelomyxa*, on the other hand, holds part of the ciliate firmly while extension of a pseudopodium beyond the food-cup pushes the rest of the prey away from the captor until the stretched organism breaks into two parts. Not only ciliates but also small Metazoa may be cut into pieces by amoebae — e.g., nematodes by *Amoeba proteus* (Mast and Root, 1915), rotifers by *Thecamoeba verrucosa* (Penard, 1905). Visible phenomena indicate that

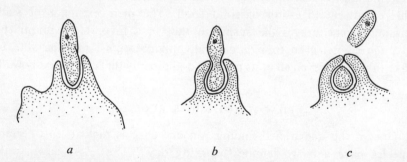

*a*                              *b*                              *c*

FIGURE 1. Amoeba proteus *feeding on* Paramecium *sp. (after Mast and Root, redrawn): (a) Food cup partially enclosing the prey. (b) Pseudopodia approaching each other and compressing the ciliate. (c) Completion of the process, leaving part of the ciliate on the outside, the rest in a food vacuole.*

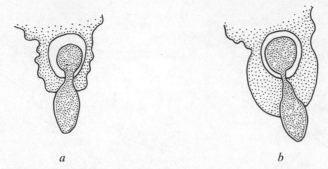

a          b

FIGURE 2. Pelomyxa carolinensis. (a) *A captured ciliate about to be bisected in a food cup.* (b) *Extension of the captor's pseudopodium is about to pull the prey into two pieces; a few seconds later, the protruding portion of the ciliate was separated from its captured half and swam away (after Kudo, redrawn).*

ingestion of food by various amoeboid phagotrophs may require a significant expenditure of energy, as in the capture of ciliates, rotifers and nematodes.

Small prey are often ingested by a sort of invagination in certain amoebae (*Dientamoeba fragilis*, etc.), the process simulating the formation of a flask-shaped cytopharynx (Figure 3) as seen in many of the more specialized Protozoa (Wenrich, 1944). In some cases the "gullet" (or cytopharynx) is formed at the tip of an extended pseudopodium. The cytostomal portion of the structure is soon obliterated by fusion of its walls, leaving the food completely enclosed in a food vacuole. An analogous type of ingestion has been described in a free-living amoeba,

a          b

FIGURE 3. *Gulletlike structure in* Dientamoeba fragilis *(after Wenrich, redrawn).* (a) *Tubular "gullet" flush with surface of body containing a partially ingested bacterium.* (b) *Opening of "gullet" at tip of a cytoplasmic extension.*

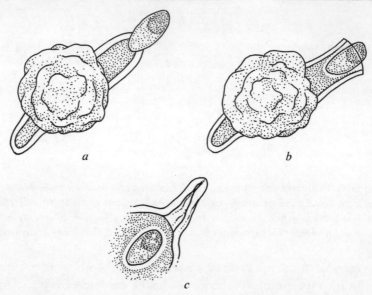

FIGURE 4. *Ingestion in* Thecamoeba sphaeronucleolus *(after Bovee*, redrawn). (a) *Captured shelled rhizopod is about to be ingested.* (b) *Ingestion well under way; tubular "gullet" quite evident; withdrawal of endoplasm in progress.* (c) *Ingestion completed; prey enclosed in food vacuole; gullet has disappeared with local fusion of pellicle.*

*Thecamoeba sphaeronucleolus* (Bovee, 1960). When the tip of an extended pseudopodium makes contact with a food organism, it sticks to the prey (Figure 4). At the point of contact, the thick pellicle of this amoeba seems to dissolve, while the underlying cytoplasm of the pseudopodium is retracted toward the body proper. The result appears to be suction. This pulls the prey into the weak spot in the pellicle and down through the tube formed by the persisting pellicle of the pseudopodium after withdrawal of the cytoplasm. The captured food passes on down the tube to make contact with the plasma membrane. Then, an invagination develops and the prey is finally enclosed in a food vacuole. The empty "gullet," or pellicular tube, soon shrivels up and eventually disappears.

In *Pelomyxa palustris* (Kudo, 1957), ingestion occurs in the posterior part of the body, which is sticky enough to trap objects making contact with it. Clear cytoplasmic projections are gradually extended around the adherent object, which is finally drawn into the body. In the case of filamentous algae, a cytoplasmic sleeve is extended to enclose a filament making contact with the body. As ingestion gets under way, the cyto-plasmic sleeve is retracted so that the free portion of the algal filament extends directly from the body surface. Ingestion of such filaments seems to be completed largely by a forward streaming of the endoplasm. As a result, an ingested filament may extend from the anterior end to the posterior end of *Pelomyxa*, with the uningested portion of the filament trailing behind the organism.

In a heliozoon, *Actinophrys sol*, an organism of suitable size (e.g., *Astasia* or a similar flagellate) may adhere to one of the slender axopodia. The captured organism is then moved, apparently by cytoplasmic flow in the pseudopodium, toward the body of the captor (Figure 5). When the prey touches the body surface, a thin cytoplasmic cup is extended to enclose the captive and a food vacuole is formed at the margin of

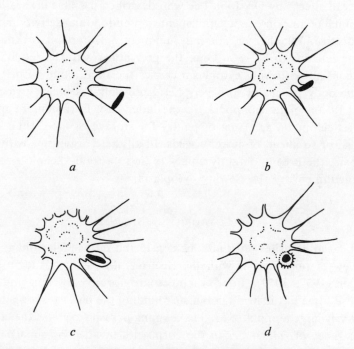

FIGURE 5. *Ingestion of a flagellate by* Actinophrys sol *(after Kitching, redrawn.) (a) Contact of flagellate with an axopodium. (b) Flagellate has moved down axopodium to make contact with the outer cytoplasm, which has extended a funnel for ingestion. (c) Flagellate now enclosed. (d) Withdrawal of "funnel" leaves flagellate in a food vacuole at surface of body.*

the captor's body. Since such a food cup is extended also in response to contact with a glass needle, this plase of ingestion evidently depends primarily upon mechanical stimulation (Kitching, 1960). In this case, the characteristic heliozoan axopodia serve as traps for the capture of food but do not function directly in the ingestion of food.

In an analogous method of capture, the slender and sticky pseudopodia (*reticulopodia*) of Foraminifera adhere to small organisms on contact. In at least some cases such contact is not exactly fortuitous. In laboratory material, certain foraminiferan species have been found to exert a fatal attraction for small flagellates, such as *Dunaliella parva*. The attraction, effective at a distance of several millimeters, causes the flagellates to swim to the reticulopodial network or to the test, depending upon the particular species which is collecting its food in this fashion (termed the "circean effect" by Dr. John Lee who described it). This invocation of a chemotactic response as a supplement to pseudopodial activity in feeding is effective. Whether or not it is uniquely a feature of foraminiferan eating remains to be seen. Once the prey adheres to the reticulopodia, the constantly flowing cytoplasm carries the food along with it, either to the body proper or to a peripheral protoplasmic mass formed by a local fusion of reticulopodia. In the latter case Foraminifera may use the reticulopodia as a sort of pantry for storage of food, thus keeping a meal or so ahead of current needs. In all these organisms with reticulopodia, the prey apparently comes to lie in a food vacuole as a result of engulfment by the flowing cytoplasm.

PHAGOTROPHY IN SPOROZOA

Malarial parasites must now be considered intracellular phagotrophs, in view of observations with the electron microscope (Rudzinska and Trager, 1957, 1959). Food vacuoles are formed by invagination to enclose some of the hemoglobin surrounding the parasite. Ingestion of a relatively large amount of food by a young parasite explains the common appearance of *ring stages* in the corpuscles invaded by such parasites. Observations on living parasites (*Plasmodium falciparum*) in blood corpuscles showed young parasites which, seen in edge view, were cup-like (Figure 6) and in surface view were typical *rings* as usually described for this species. The interior of the ring apparently corresponds to the food vacuole containing ingested hemoglobin. Digestion of the hemo-

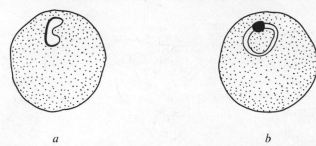

*a*                                          *b*

FIGURE 6. Plasmodium falciparum *in red corpuscles of human host.* (a) *Edge view of parasite, living material (after Rudzinska and Trager, redrawn).* (b) *Surface view of "ring stage," stained material (schematic).*

globin leaves a certain amount of residual hematin, the malarial "pigment" in erythrocytic stages of *Plasmodium* spp. These observations on malarial parasites cleared up the previously puzzling phenomenon of "absorption" of such cytoplasmic proteins as hemoglobin by supposedly saprozoic parasites. In spite of their intracellular habitat, malarial parasites would seem to be at least as much phagotrophic as saprozoic. Another type of intracellular blood parasite, *Babesia rodhaini*, perhaps somewhat distantly related to the malarial parasites, also ingests hemoglobin of invaded corpuscles (Rudzinska and Trager, 1962) but the heme component apparently is broken down so that there is no residual pigment (*hemozoin*) like that found in *Plasmodium*. Other Sporozoa also may be phagotrophic. Phagotrophy has been reported, for example, in such gregarines as *Monocystis banyulensis* which ingest tissue cells of the host, at least occasionally.

### PHAGOTROPHY IN FLAGELLATES

Some of the flagellates ingest food through a temporary cytostome and gullet not unlike the structures seen in some of the amoebae. *Monas vestita*, one of the colorless Chrysomonadida, is an excellent example (Reynolds, 1934). Appropriate stimulation, either contact with a particle of food or a tap by the longer flagellum, causes the body to extend a funnel-like food cup which serves as a mouth and gullet (Figure 7). The prey seems to be drawn into this "gullet" by suction, sometimes helped by a push from the flagellum. The protoplasmic projection quickly closes at the distal end to form a food vacuole enclosing the

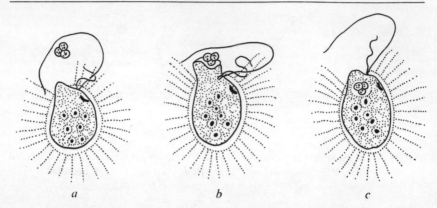

*a*          *b*          *c*

FIGURE 7. *Ingestion in* Monas vestita *(after Reynolds, redrawn). (a) Longer flagellum steering food toward anterior end of body. (b) Extension of food cup as food reaches body. (c) Food ingested and enclosed in food vacuole. This flagellate is covered with a "gelatinous" layer through which delicate strands extend radially.*

captured organism. A somewhat similar temporary gullet has been described in *Histomonas meleagridis* (Figure 8), a parasite of domestic birds (Wenrich, 1943).

In such choanoflagellates as *Codonosiga* (*Codosiga*) *botrytis* a sheath, continuous with the stalk and covering the body, takes the place of the "funnel" seen in *Monas*. As flagellar activity drives particles of food toward the body, the anterior part of the body is pulled away from the

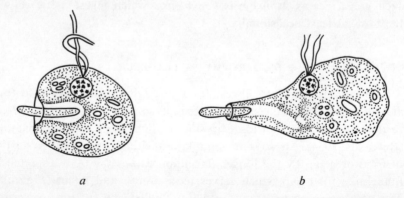

*a*                    *b*

FIGURE 8. *Temporary "gullet" in* Histomonas meleagridis *(after Wenrich, redrawn). (a) Partly ingested bacterium in gullet opening at surface of body. (b) Elongated gullet in a snoutlike projection from the body.*

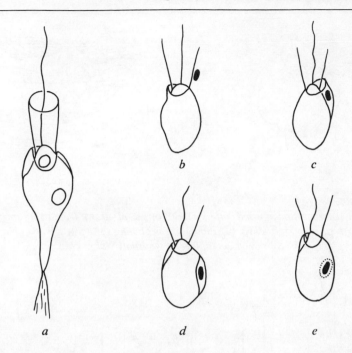

FIGURE 9. *Ingestion in* Codonosiga botrytis *(after Lapage, redrawn).* (a) *Sessile stage showing collar, mucous envelope, anterior nucleus, contractile vacuole.* (b) *Food particle being driven down outside of collar to the body.* (c) *Contraction of the body away from the mucous sheath has left a pocket into which the food drops.* (d, e) *Expansion of body toward sheath forces the food into the cytoplasm — a sort of "forced invagination."*

sheath. This leaves a space into which food particles can drop (Figure 9). The body then pushes forward against the sheath, thus trapping the food which soon appears in a food vacuole formed presumably by invagination (Lapage, 1925).

In *Leidyopsis* sp. and *Trichonympha campanula*, intestinal flagellates of termites, ingestion of wood chips at the posterior end of the body has been observed (Swezy, 1923). Both types of flagellates have been seen extending pseudopodia which adhere to wood chips and pull them toward the body surface where ingestion occurs (Figure 10), apparently by a process resembling the invagination described in various amoebae. The size of the ingested material sometimes equals or exceeds that of the eater.

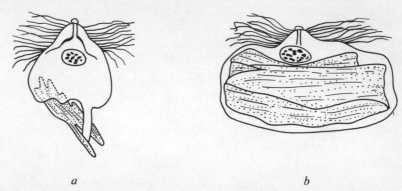

*a*                                                              *b*

FIGURE 10.   *Ingestion of wood chips by* Leidyopsis *sp.; drawn from living specimens*
*(after Swezy,* redrawn). (a) *Flagellate beginning to ingest a wood chip.*
(b) *Specimen containing an unusually large chip.*

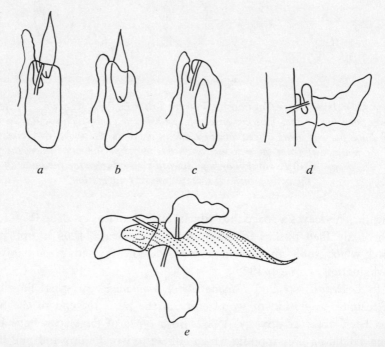

*a*              *b*              *c*              *d*

*e*

FIGURE 11. Peranema trichophorum, *feeding activities (after Chen,* redrawn).
(a, b, c) *Stages in ingestion of an intact* Euglena *sp.* (d) P. trichophorum *attached*
*to a large specimen of* E. spirogyra, *feeding by puncture and subsequent suction*
*of protoplasm from the body of the prey.* (e) *Three specimens of* P. trichophorum
*sharing a large* E. spirogyra; *one of the phagotrophs has started*
*a swallowing job it will be unable to finish.*

In certain phagotrophic euglenoid flagellates (*Peranema, Heteronema,* etc.) an accessory "rod apparatus" has been developed in connection with the gullet. This apparatus (Figure 11) seems to be useful especially for puncturing the body wall of prey not small enough to be swallowed (Chen, 1950; Tannreuther, 1923). In such a case, the contents of the captured organism, after the pellicle is punctured, are ingested by suction and food vacuoles are formed at the base of the gullet. However, these flagellates may do rather well without resorting to puncture and suction, as in the occasional ingestion of an intact specimen of *Euglena* by *Heteronema acus* or *Peranema trichophorum* (Figure 11).

### PHAGOTROPHY IN CILIATES

In general, ciliates are the Protozoa which have made the most progress in development of specialized organelles for capture and ingestion of prey. Most of these accessory buccal organelles are structures formed essentially by the fusion of cilia or by the grouping of cilia into thickset bands.

In some ciliates, usually considered fairly primitive, the cytostome opens directly onto the surface of the body and there may be no accessory feeding organelles of the usual kind. However, the cytopharynx is sometimes surrounded by a zone of rod – like *trichites* with their anterior ends lying in the cortex encircling the cytostome (Figure 12). It is believed that, in at least some of these ciliates, the trichites are tipped

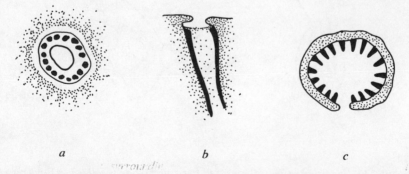

a        b        c

FIGURE 12. *Trichites surrounding the gullet in certain ciliates (after Wetzel; redrawn).* (a) *End view of* Coleps hirtus, *showing tips of trichites surrounding gullet.* (b) *Longitudinal section of gullet in* Nassula aurea, *showing two trichites extending along the wall.* (c) *Cross section of* N. aurea, *showing trichites encircling the gullet.*

with toxic substances capable of paralyzing prey and thus facilitating ingestion.

Ciliates with a mouth opening directly onto the body surface usually eat fairly large microorganisms. *Perispira ovum*, for example, ingests euglenoid flagellates (Dewey and Kidder, 1940), the captured organisms apparently being taken in by suction (Figure 13*a*). *Didinium nasutum* does an even more impressive job in ingesting its most commonly eaten prey, specimens of *Paramecium* which may be much larger than their captor (Figure 13).

*Dileptus anser* is another voracious eater. In addition to an array of small organisms which even include rotifers, this ciliate under laboratory

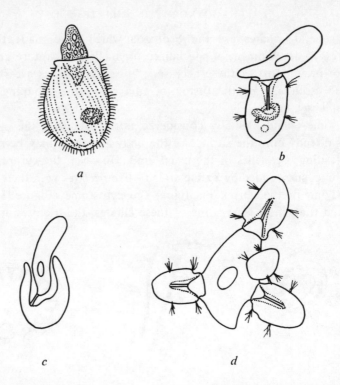

FIGURE 13. *Ingestion in two ciliates.* (a) Perispira ovum *swallowing* Euglena *sp.* (*after Dewey and Kidder, redrawn*). (b, c) Didinium nasutum *ingesting* Paramecium *sp., early and later stages; note "seizing organ" attached to body of prey.* (d) *A gang of small* D. nasutum *have brought down a large specimen of* Paramecium *sp.*

conditions will eat such unaccustomed food as chopped liver and injured oligochaetes, small clams or nematodes (Brown and Jenkins, 1962). Although small planarian worms also may be eaten, a steady diet of flatworms results in giant *Dileptus* which are not only over-stuffed but also are seemingly unhealthy (Janovy, 1962).

Ciliates which normally feed on small microorganisms such as bacteria are usually equipped with buccal organelles for sweeping such particles into the cytostome. In these cases, the cytostome opens into some sort of a buccal cavity equipped with various organelles (membrane, membranelles, or sometimes thickset bands of cilia) for creating appropriate currents in the medium. The buccal cavity, in turn, may or may not open out into a depression in the body wall, a peristomial area (or "vestibulum"). This region ranges from a long trough to a shallow pit in different ciliates and is equipped with no organelles other than the usual somatic ciliature of the species.

The buccal apparatus of *Tetrahymena* is representative of many ciliates which have a buccal cavity but no specialized peristomial area. The buccal organelles include a *membrane*, extending along the outer right margin of the buccal cavity, and three *membranelles* lying toward the left in the dorsolateral wall of the buccal cavity (Figure 14). The activity of these organelles creates a current driving particles to the cytostome,

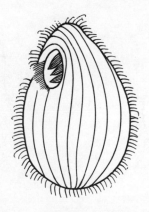

FIGURE 14. Tetrahymena pyriformis. *Illustration shows buccal organelles: membrane and 3 membranelles; somatic cilia shown only at margin of organism, solid lines represent other rows of cilia.*

which lies at the posterior end of the buccal cavity. As the ingested food particles accumulate, the deeper end of the cytopharynx is expanded to form a bulb-like enlargement for reception of the food. When enough has been collected, this enlarged end of the cytopharynx is pinched off to form a food vacuole which floats about in the cytoplasm.

The possession of a mouth of the *Tetrahymena* type, apparently adapted primarily to the ingestion of bacteria and other small micro-organisms, does not necessarily prevent a ciliate from indulging an appetite for meat. *Tetrahymena corlissi*, for example, can be maintained on chopped beef as a steady diet, and this species will also eat pieces of raw worms. Such a taste has been applied to the task of isolating setae from earthworms (Harman and Corliss, 1956). When fed appropriate pieces of fresh or frozen earthworms, the ciliates eat the flesh and leave the setae cleaned free of tissue. *Tetrahymena vorax* is another example of a ciliate with rather flexible feeding habits. In a completely soluble axenic medium, these ciliates are usually moderate in size and have a fairly small mouth, much like that of *T. pyriformis*. When they are forced, by lack of other food, to eat living *T. pyriformis* (Kidder, Lilly and Claff, 1940), the ciliates take to the change in diet with no apparent difficulty by developing a large mouth and growing into a giant form, or "macro-stome" type (Figure 15).

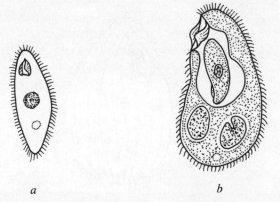

*a*                    *b*

FIGURE 15. Tetrahymena vorax, *"microstome" and "macrostome" types; after Kidder, Lilly and Claff*, redrawn). (a) *Microstome type from broth culture.* (b) *Macrostome type of moderate size containing a freshly ingested ciliate* (Colpidium *sp.*).

A somewhat comparable effect of diet on size of the body also has been noted in an amoeba, *Mayorella cultura* (Bovee, 1960a). Well fed specimens were plump and much bulkier than specimens kept on a skimpy diet. However, there was no significant change in form of the pseudopodia or in their behavior. Also, there was little or no change in length of the pseudopodia; starvation merely reduced their girth, just as for the body as a whole. The food supply may thus influence the size of the eater in both amoebae and ciliates, but without fundamental modification of the basic morphological features which characterize a species.

A version of buccal organelles for eating small microorganisms, somewhat different from the *Tetrahymena* type, is found in *Paramecium*. A long groove begins near the anterior end and leads diagonally and posteriorly to a pouch-like buccal cavity. The buccal organelles include three types of structures: (1) a small membrane on the right outer margin of the cavity, corresponding apparently to the membrane in *Tetrahymena;* (2) a dorsolateral band containing four rows of fairly long cilia and extending almost to the cytostome; and (3) two more or less separate bands of closely set cilia extending from an antero-dorsal origin toward the posteroventral wall of the buccal cavity. The apparatus is well adapted to its task of driving small food particles into the cytostome.

In the hypotrichs (*Euplotes, Stylonychia*, etc.) the buccal organelles are more specialized than in *Tetrahymena*. There is still a membrane on the right in the more generalized hypotrichs but this buccal organelle has been lost in a number of genera. The membranelles, which lie in a long row on the left, are much more numerous than in *Tetrahymena* and apparently make a very efficient mechanism for collection of small microorganisms.

Suctorian ciliates have perfected a method of feeding by means of tentacles which seem to suck food into the body. A suctorial tentacle ends in a terminal bulb covered with an amorphous and probably sticky material. Inside the tentacle an inner tube extends from the bulb into the body of the organism. In at least certain species, the wall of this tube contains fibrils resembling the contractile myonemes seen in various other ciliates. The tip of the tentacle adheres to the prey, which normally is a living ciliate. Although certain ciliates seem to be less satisfactory than others for particular suctorian species, the basis for this apparent selectivity is not yet known.

The stimulus inducing activity of the tentacles apparently is a substance, or perhaps a combination of substances, present in the body wall of ciliates. Activity has been induced in the laboratory by tempting the organisms with small pieces of agar enriched with a ciliate homogenate (Hull, 1961). Synthetic enrichments containing peptone, acetylcholine, glutathione and a few salts seem to be almost as effective as the ciliate homogenate. Whatever these tasty substances are, they seem to be lacking in flagellates because suctoria typically do not feed on such organisms.

Soon after a tentacle adheres to a ciliate, there is typically an enzymatic or mechanical rupture of the body wall of the prey. Protoplasm next starts flowing down the tentacle into the suctorian cytoplasm (Figure 16). A food vacuole is soon formed from the inner end of each tube in much the same manner as from the gullet of more typical ciliates. The process is continued until the contents of the prey have been ingested. Much less commonly, at least some of the Suctorida can ingest an entire flagellate or ciliate if the prey is not too large.

The mechanics of suctorial feeding are not yet fully understood. In certain species, but not in others, contractions of the wall of the inner tube have suggested a sort of peristalsis during ingestion. Another inter-

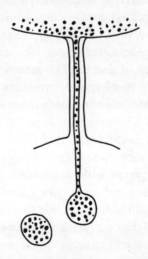

FIGURE 16. Tokophrya lemnarum *feeding on a captured ciliate; cytoplasm of the prey is flowing down a tentacle into a developing food vacuole (after Noble, redrawn).*

pretation is that the tentacles exert a real suction which is responsible for ingestion (Kitching, 1954). Expansion of the suctorian body might be partly responsible for such suction, as has been suggested. An increased frequency of vacuolar contraction, known to occur during feeding in at least a few species, also might create enough negative pressure to account for appreciable suction. Another suggested possibility, which might be significant during expansion of the suctorian body, is that a positive pressure, exerted by the medium on the prey, forces material down a tentacle after rupture of the body wall. Whatever the responsible mechanism, the ingested food soon reached the inner end of the tentacle, where a food vacuole is developed.

### THE FOOD VACUOLE IN PHAGOTROPHS

During the ingestion of solid food, the material becomes enclosed in a food vacuole, sometimes known as a gastric vacuole (gastriole) in deference to its function. At this point, the ingested food is still suspended in fluid from the culture medium taken in with the solid particles. However, in the case of ciliates which ingest large prey the amount of external medium incorporated in the food vacuole is often insignificant. In order to assimilate such ingested food, the phagotroph must first digest the material. The necessary hydrolysis takes place in the food vacuole, as indicated by obvious changes in solid food which has been ingested. In such representative phagotrophs as species of *Amoeba*, *Actinosphaerium* and *Paramecium*, the pH of the vacuolar contents soon drops to about 4.0. Changes responsible for this change in pH are still unidentified, but there is no direct evidence that the phagotroph actually secretes acids into the vacuole. Such a secretion has been suggested for *Bresslaua insidiatrix* (Claff, Dewey, and Kidder, 1941) as well as for other ciliates by earlier investigators. However, Mast (1942) insisted that in *Amoeba* respiration of the enclosed prey and chemical changes accompanying death were responsible, rather than any secretion of acid into the food vacuole. In *Amoeba dubia* which had ingested vitally stained flagellates, the prey showed a decrease in pH before there was any comparable change in the vacuolar fluid. At any rate, digestion gets under way before long, as indicated by changes in microscopic appearance of the vacuolar contents, and the pH of the vacuolar fluid rises as digestion begins.

Cytological observations on certain phagotrophs have detected the aggregation of small cytoplasmic inclusions ("digestive granules") on the outer surfaces of the young food vacuole. It has been assumed by various workers over the past seventy years that these visible phenomena represent stages in the secretion of digestive enzymes into the vacuole. This interpretation might not conflict with the observed migration of globules to the surface of the food vacuole, where they form an adherent layer in such ciliates as *Paramecium* (Dunihue, 1931). A similar layer of granules has been described also in the carnivorous *Bresslaua insidiatrix* (Claff, Dewey, and Kidder, 1941). Such a layer of globules eventually disappears after digestion is under way but this is scarcely conclusive evidence for the conversion of inactive "globules" into active digestive enzymes.

At any rate, food is digested within the vacuole to products which can be used in metabolism. If undigested residues remain, such useless materials are eliminated sooner or later, usually through a more or less specific point (*cytopyge*) in the body wall of ciliates but at any convenient point in the case of amoeboid organisms.

The production of specific kinds of digestive enzymes has been investigated in a few Protozoa. The ability of the ciliate, *Tetrahymena pyriformis*, to digest gelatin and casein has been known for many years and properties of the digestive enzymes of this species have been investigated to a limited extent. More recently, it has been found (Viswanatha and Liener, 1956) that this ciliate digests cooked albumen and soy protein much more readily than the raw materials, although uncooked casein and fibrinogen are readily attacked. Peptidases also have been reported in other ciliates, including species of *Frontonia* and *Paramecium*. Phagotrophic Sarcodina (*Amoeba, Pelomyxa, Physarum*) likewise have been shown to produce proteinases, as everyone had suspected. Among the Sporozoa, proteinases were reported in malarial parasites (Moulder and Evans, 1946) some years before phagotrophy was reported in these organisms.

The ability to digest polysaccharides also is known for various ciliates and flagellates and may be inferred, on the basis of feeding habits, for many Sarcodina. Some of the termite flagellates as well as certain ciliates living in the rumen of herbivores can digest cellulose, an ability which the tissues of their hosts do not possess. A similar digestive ability may be assumed for the herbivorous Protozoa which feed on algae.

### SAPROZOIC NUTRITION

Saprozoic feeding is a method long attributed to Protozoa without any apparent mouth or any pseudopodial method of ingestion. A truly saprozoic organism obviously would have a somewhat restricted diet because it could depend only upon those materials which pass through the protozoan pellicle and plasma membrane. Furthermore, the specific identity of such materials might vary significantly under different environmental conditions, since such factors as pH of the medium may influence the rate of uptake of metabolically important substrates. For example, the uptake by *Polytomella caeca* of such substrates as acetate, butyrate, propionate, succinate and valerate is influenced by pH of the medium, and the relationship becomes more and more apparent as the concentration of substrate is increased. Starting with acetate at 0.1 per cent, a tenfold increase narrows the pH range for utilization from 3.9–9.2 to 7.4–7.8, and a comparable increase in *n*-butyrate narrows the range from pH 4.6–7.2 to pH 7.2. In contrast to the acid substrates, absorption of the corresponding alcohols is independent of pH (Wise, 1961).

Little is known about uptake mechanisms in Protozoa but there are indications that the process occasionally can involve something other than simple diffusion. This may be true even for certain metal ions, since *Acanthamoeba* sp. takes up potassium against a concentration gradient (Klein, 1961). Some of the phytoflagellates, such as *Euglena*, likewise are known to concentrate phosphorus to a very striking degree against such a concentration gradient. In the case of sugars, *Tetrahymena pyriformis* does not take up the metabolically useless arabinose against a concentration difference. However, the uptake is inhibited competitively by glucose and is characterized by a high $Q_{10}$ value, and thus could not really be considered a simple diffusion. Cirillo (1962) has termed this type of uptake a "facilitated diffusion," comparable to the process he has observed in yeast. Data accumulated on *Crithidia luciliae* (Min and Cosgrove, 1963) indicate that this species has an active transport mechanism for monosaccharides and that the mechanism shows maximal activity when the exogenous concentration of sugar is low. The flagellates take up not only useful sugars but also a number of monosaccharides which cannot be catabolized. The latter accumulate as such in internal solution, whereas the metabolically useful ones do not accumulate in free form. Only monosaccharides entered *C. luciliae*. Useful disaccharides and oligosaccharides were first hydrolyzed externally to monosaccharides. Observations on *Polytomella caeca*, a phytomonad flagellate, suggest an active absorption of acetate through the plasma membrane (Wise, 1961).

PINOCYTOSIS

Pinocytosis, a term coined by Lewis for a process of "drinking" by cells, has been observed in Protozoa as diverse as amoebae and ciliates. In various amoebae (Mast and Doyle, 1934; Holter, 1959; Roth, 1960), the essential morphological feature of pinocytosis is the formation of delicate tubular invaginations of the surface layer, followed by a pinching off of one or more pinocytosis vacuoles from the inner end of each tubule (Figure 17). In an amoeba, production of such narrow tubes requires only a few seconds, although each may remain visible for several minutes. These invaginations, in at least several observed cases, are formed by fusion of small protuberances to produce a tube open at its distal end. The mound containing this little tube is extended as a small pseudopodium while the tube itself increases in length at the same time. One or more pinocytosis vacuoles are soon produced at the inner end of each tubule and are then set free in the cytoplasm. "Drinking" seems to be intermittent rather than continuous, and the process is stimulated by certain substances (*inducers*) which are dissolved in the

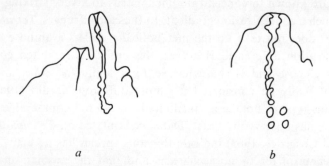

a                              b

FIGURE 17. *Formation of pinocytosis vacuoles in an amoeba (after Mast and Doyle, schematic). (a) Early and late stages in formation of pinocytosis tubules. (b) Older tubule, small vacuoles being pinched off at inner end.*

external.medium. The better inducers include such substances as gelatin, albumin, gamma-globulin, glutamate, ribonuclease, and even certain salts, but not such foods as carbohydrates. Furthermore, certain inducers (toluidine blue, for example) cannot represent foods. In *Amoeba proteus*, pinocytosis seems to be dependent upon aerobic respiration and is retarded by low temperatures (DeTerra and Rustad, 1959).

As for the essential properties of substances inducing pinocytosis, it is known that at least some of these inducers do not readily penetrate the protozoan body wall. Whether this characteristic is the only one of major importance is doubtful. It has been suggested (Marshall *et al.*, 1959) that pinocytosis begins with the binding of an inducer at the body surface, the "essential groups of the bound substance being positively charged, those on the cell surface being negative. Several characteristics suggest that the binding is saltlike." All inducers tested on *Chaos chaos* proved to be positively charged molecules (Brandt, 1958), the activity depending to some extent upon concentration of the inducer in solution. Proteins labeled with fluorescent dyes were adsorbed to the pellicle, while salts serving as inducers caused a swelling of the outer layer of this membrane. The weakened membrane was then drawn into the cytoplasm by its "points of attachment" to the plasmagel, forming an invagination later to be separated from the surface membrane as a pinocytosis vacuole. Since noninducers in solution may be taken in during pinocytosis stimulated by an inducer, the apparent discrimination against such foods as carbohydrates might be no serious handicap under appropriate conditions even if the body wall were actually impermeable to these substances in the absence of pinocytosis. For example, it has been found that, after feeding a mixture of $C^{14}$-glucose and $\gamma$-globulin to amoebae, labeling of the cytoplasm was detected in about 45 minutes. When the radioactive glucose alone was fed, no pinocytosis was observed and no labeling of the cytoplasm could be detected until about 22 hours had elapsed (Chapman-Andresen and Holter, 1955).

Some time after the formation of typical food vacuoles in phagocytosis, a comparable process ("micropinocytosis") may occur at the surface of a food vacuole, which originally had a smooth surface. Such internal pinocytosis has been described in *Pelomyxa* (Roth, 1960), in *Glaucoma chattoni* (Holz, *et al.*, 1961), and in *Paramecium aurelia* (Jurand, 1961). The frequent appearance of protuberances at the surface of the older vacuoles and the appearance of small secondary vacuoles around the food vacuoles suggested that the secondary vacuoles arise by pinocytosis from the former. It was believed that pinocytosis at the food vacuole may be significant in the assimilation of digested food, perhaps by increasing the surface area available for absorption. Roth calculated that in *Pelomyxa* the increase in surface area might be on the order of 300 times.

The membrane of the cytopharynx in *P. aurelia* apparently shows a similar formation of vacuoles by pinocytosis (Jurand, 1961). Such a formation of small vacuoles occurs also in *Glaucoma chattoni* (Holz *et al.*, 1961). As in other cases of pinocytosis, the production of such vacuoles is stimulated by particular substances in solution.

The formation of regular food vacuoles in phagotrophic organisms maintained in a non-particulate medium may, like pinocytosis, depend upon the presence of an inducer. *Tetrahymena pyriformis* shows very few food vacuoles in a completely soluble defined medium (Seaman, 1961). Apparently, the difference between pinocytosis and phagocytosis may be more nearly quantitative than qualitative.

In electron micrographs of *Trypanosoma mega* a cytostome and gullet have been observed in these supposedly saprozoic flagellates (Steinert and Novikoff, 1960). After suspension of the flagellates in a solution of ferritin, sections of the organisms showed vacuoles in the cytoplasm surrounding the gullet. It was suspected that these vacuoles were formed by pinocytosis from the lining of the slender gullet.

One effect of pinocytosis, whether at the surface of the body or the surface of a food vacuole, would obviously be an increase in area of the surface involved, thus increasing rates of diffusion. However, additional factors are probably involved in any benefits derived from pinocytosis. It has been suggested that in amoebae there is a physical modification of the surface layer at the time pinocytosis is taking place and that this change favors in some way the additional uptake of foods that otherwise might be only slowly available or almost unavailable otherwise (Roth, 1960).

Definitive evaluation of pinocytosis (Holter, 1959) probably depends upon determining how such materials as proteins are transferred from the pinocytosis vacuoles to the cytoplasm. In other words, how does this material which the organism drinks get into the cytoplasm, presumably without preliminary digestion? Or does digestion first occur within the pinocytosis vacuoles, to be followed by diffusion into the cytoplasm? At present, there is no conclusive evidence for or against the occurrence of digestion within the pinocytosis vacuoles. A change in permeability of the vacuolar membrane may, as some workers suspect, be responsible for loss of the contents to the cytoplasm. In any case, the pinocytosis vacuoles gradually become smaller and smaller until it is difficult or impossible to distinguish them from other small cytoplasmic inclusions (Chapman-Andresen and Nilsson, 1960). So far as functional significance is concerned, Holter (1959) felt that pinocytosis is a fundamental physiological process in amoeboid cells, although the term (which implies "drinking") is becoming less appropriate as the importance of particular solutes (inducers), rather than the solvent, becomes more apparent. Pinocytosis may turn out to be closely related to the general problem of active uptake of substrates from the medium. Obviously, the general nutritional significance of pinocytosis deserves further investigation since it seems to be quantitatively as well as qualitatively significant, even in distinctly phagotrophic organisms.

## Bibliography

BOVEE, E. C., 1956. Some observations on a marine ameba of intertidal zones, *Vexillifera telmathalassa* n. sp. J. PROTOZOOL. **3**, 155–158;

————— 1960. Studies of feeding behavior of amebas. I. Ingestion of thecate rhizopods and flagellates by verrucosid amebas, particularly *Thecamoeba sphaeronucleolus*. *J. Protozool.* **7**, 55–60.

————— 1950a. Studies concerning the effects of nutrition on morphology of amebas. I. *Mayorella cultura* Bovee, on abundant and starvation quantities. *Amer. Midl. Nat.* **63**, 257–269.

BRANDT, P. W., 1958. A study of the mechanism of pinocytosis. *Exper. Cell Res.* **15**, 300–313.

BROWN, H. P. and M. M. Jenkins 1962. A protozoon (*Dileptus:* Ciliata) predatory upon Metazoa. *Science* **136**, 710.

CHAPMAN-ANDRESEN, C., and H. HOLTER 1955. Studies on the ingestion of $C^{14}$ glucose by pinocytosis in the amoeba. *Exper. Cell Res., Suppl.* **3**, 52–63.

CHAPMAN-ANDRESEN, C., and J. R. NILSSON 1960. Electron micrographs of pinocytosis channels in *Amoeba proteus*. *Exper. Cell Res.* **19**, 631–633.

CHEN, Y. T., 1950. Investigations on the biology of *Peranema trichophorum* (Euglenineae). *Quart. J. Micr. Sci.* **91**, 279–308.

CIRILLO, V. C., 1962. Mechanism of arabinose transport in *Tetrahymena pyriformis. J. Bact.* **84**, 754–758.

CLAFF, C. L., V. C. DEWEY, and G. W. KIDDER, 1941. Feeding mechanisms and nutrition in three species of *Bresslaua*. *Biol. Bull*. **81**, 221–234.

DeTERRA, N. and R. C. RUSTAD, 1959. The dependence of pinocytosis on temperature and aerobic respiration. *Exper. Cell Res*. **12**, 191–195.

DEWEY, V. C., and G. W. KIDDER, 1940. Growth studies on ciliates. VI. Diagnosis, sterilization and growth characteristics of *Perispira ovum. Biol. Bull*. **79**, 255–271.

DUNIHUE, F. W., 1931. The vacuome and the neutral red reaction in *Paramecium caudatum. Arch. f. Protistenk*. **75**, 476–497.

HARMAN, W. J., and J. O. CORLISS, 1956. Isolation of earthworm setae by the use of histophagous Protozoa. *Trans. Amer. Micr. Soc*. **75**, 332–333.

HOLTER, H., 1959. Problems of pinocytosis, with special reference to amoebae. *Ann. N. Y. Acad. Sci*. **78**, 524–537

HOLZ, G. G., Jr., B. WAGNER, J. ERWIN, and D. KESSLER, 1961. The nutrition of *Glaucoma chattoni* A. *J. Protozool*. **8**, 192–199.

HULL, R. W., 1961. Studies on suctorian protozoa: the mechanism of prey adherence. *J. Protozool*. **8**, 343–350.

JANOVY, T., JR., 1963. Monsterism in *Dileptus* (Ciliata) fed on planarians (*Dugesia tigrina*). *J. Protozool*. **10**, 428–430.

JOHNSON, D. F., 1936. Growth of *Glaucoma ficaria* Kahl in cultures with single species of other microorganisms. *Arch. f. Protistenk*., **86**, 359–378.

JURAND, A., 1961. An electron microscope study of food vacuoles in *Paramecium aurelia. J. Protozool*. **8**, 125–130.

KIDDER, G. W., D. M. LILLY, and C. L. CLAFF, 1940. Growth studies on ciliates. IV. The influence of food on the structure and growth of *Glaucoma vorax* sp. nov. *Biol. Bull*. **78**, 9–23.

KITCHING, J. A., 1954. On suction in Suctoria. *Proc. 7th Symposium Colston Res. Soc*. **7**, 197–203.

———— 1960. Responses of the heliozoon *Actinophrys sol* to prey, to mechanical stimulation, and to solutions of proteins and certain other chemical substances. *J. Exper. Biol*. **37**, 407–416.

KLEIN, R. L., 1961. Homeostatic mechanisms for cation regulation in *Acanthamoeba* sp. *Exper. Cell Res*. **25**, 571–584.

KUDO, R. R., 1946. *Pelomyxa carolinensis* Wilson I. General observations on the Illinois stock. *J. Morph*. **78**, 317–351.

———— 1957. *Pelomyxa palustris* Greef. I. Cultivation and general observations. *J. Protozool*. **4**, 154–164.

LAPAGE, G., 1925. Notes on the chaonoflagellate, *Codosiga botrytis* Ehrbg. *Quart. J. Micr. Sci*. **69**, 471–508.

MARSHALL, J. W., JR., V. N. SCHUMAKER, and P. W. BRANDT, 1959. Pinocytosis in amoebae. *Ann. N. Y. Ac. Sci*. **78**, 515–523.

MAST, S. O., 1909. The reactions of *Didinium nasutum* with special reference to the feeding habits and the function of trichocysts. *Biol. Bull*. **16**, 91–118.

———— 1942. The hydrogen ion concentration of the content of the food vacuoles and the cytoplasm in *Amoeba* and other phenomena concerning the food vacuoles. *Biol. Bull*. **83**, 173–204.

MAST, S. O., and W. L. DOYLE, 1934. Ingestion of fluid by amoeba. *Protoplasma* **20**, 555–560.

MAST, S. O., and F. M. ROOT, 1916. Observations on amoeba feeding on rotifers, nematodes and ciliates, and their bearing on the surface-tension theory. *J. Exper. Zool.* **21**, 33–49.

MIN, H. S., and W. B. COSGROVE, 1963. Entrance of carbohydrate into cells of *Crithidia luciliae*. *J. Protozool.* **10**, Suppl.: 19.

MOULDER, J. W., and E. A. EVANS, JR., 1946. The biochemistry of the malaria parasite. VI. Studies on the nitrogen metabolism of the malaria parasite. *J. Biol. Chem.* **164**, 145–157.

PENARD, E., 1905. Observations sur les amibes a pellicule. *Arch. f. Protistenk.* **6**, 175–206.

REYNOLDS, B. D., 1934. Studies on monad flagellates. *Arch f. Protistenk.* **81**, 399–411.

ROTH, L. E., 1960. Electron microscopy of pinocytosis and food vacuoles in *Pelomyxa*. *J. Protozool.* **7**, 176–185.

RUDZINSKA, M. A., and W. TRAGER, 1957. Intracellular phagotrophy by malarial parasites: an electron microscope study of *Plasmodium lophurae*. *J. Protozool.* **4**, 190–199.

———— 1959, Phagotrophy and two new structures in the malaria parasite *Plasmodium berghei*. *J. Biophys. Biochem. Cytol.* **6**, 103–112.

———— 1962. Intracellular phagotrophy in *Babesia rodhaini* as revealed by electron microscopy. *J. Protozool.* **9**, 279–288.

SANDON, H., 1932. The food of Protozoa. *Publ. Fac. Sci.*, No. 1, Egypt. Univ., 197 pp.

SEAMAN, G. R., 1961. Some aspects of phagotrophy in *Tetrahymena*. *J. Protozool.* **8**, 204–212.

STEINERT, M., and A. B. NOVIKOFF, 1960. The existence of a cytostome and the occurrence of pinocytosis in the trypanosome, *Trypanosoma mega*. *J. Biophys. Biochem. Cytol.* **8**, 563–569.

SWEZY, O., 1923. The pseudopodial method of feeding by trichonymphid flagellates in wood-eating termites. *Univ. Calif. Publ. Zool.* **20**, 391–400.

TANNREUTHER, G. W., 1923. Nutrition and reproduction in *Euglena*. *Arch. f. Entwickl., Orig.* **52**, 367–383.

VISWANATHA, T. and I. E. LIENER, 1956. Isolation and properties of a proteinase from *Tetrahymena pyriformis W*. *Arch. Biochem. Biophys.* **61**, 410–421.

WENRICH, D. H., 1943. Observations on the morphology of *Histomonas* (Protozoa) from wild pheasants and chickens. *J. Morph.* **72**, 279–303.

———— 1944. Studies on *Dientamoeba fragilis* (Protozoa). IV. Further observations with an outline of present-day knowledge of this species. *J. Parasitol.* **30**, 322–338.

WISE, D. L., 1961. Absorption of acid nutrients by an acetate flagellate. *J. Protozool.* **8**, Suppl.: 8–9.

# 3. Foods Used by Protozoa

## Variety in Protozoan Diets

Protozoa which are not dependent upon solid food may utilize quite a variety of materials, and the favorite menu can vary from one species to another. A medium (Provasoli and McLaughlin, 1963) found satisfactory for a marine dinoflagellate, *Amphidinium carteri*, contains sodium nitrate, dipotassium phosphate, magnesium sulfate, sodium chloride, calcium chloride, a group of trace metals (B, Co, Cu, Fe, Mn and Zn, plus the chelating agent, EDTA), a pH buffer, and three vitamins (biotin, $B_{12}$, thiamine). Since these flagellates contain chromatophores, the basic energy source is light. A phytoflagellate without chromatophores must have some organic source of energy, such as ethanol, acetate, or other suitable carbon compound, since no protozoon is known to obtain all its energy from any inorganic food.

Except for differences in salinity, which are correlated with ecological distribution and influence nutrition only indirectly, marine and fresh-water phytoflagellates show similar requirements on the whole. However, chlorophyll-bearing and colorless species obviously differ with respect to the energy source, and in both physiological groups there are

30

differences in abilities to synthesize vitamins. As noted above, *Amphidinium carteri* needs three vitamins; certain other chlorophyll-bearing flagellates need none. Analogous differences have been reported among colorless phytoflagellates, although ability to synthesize vitamins is more likely to be limited than in chlorophyll-bearing species.

Outside the group of phytoflagellates, the diet of heterotrophs is more complex, reflecting inabilities to synthesize a wider variety of the materials needed in metabolism. For example, *Leishmania tarentolae*, a trypanosomid flagellate, needs at least 15 amino acids (Trager, 1957a) — a marked contrast to a phytoflagellate which can use an ammonium salt or a nitrate for synthesis of all its nitrogenous components. Representative heterotrophs in groups other than the flagellates grow in media more or less comparable to those supporting growth of *L. tarentolae*. *Paramecium multimicronucleatum*, for example, needs 13 amino acids for growth in a non-particulate medium (Johnson and Miller, 1957).

Phagotrophs maintained in particulate media, a more nearly natural environment than a chemically defined medium containing only known materials in solution, also show a variety in their "preferred" foods. Herbivorous types, some of which have to get along with a small mouth which limits the size of microorganisms normally ingested, may feed primarily on bacteria, small algae, or similar organisms. However, such restrictions on size are not the only factors affecting herbivores. Some bacteria eaters show decided "preferences" in that certain species of bacteria support more vigorous growth than others. For instance, *Tetrahymena pyriformis* grew fairly well through 30 transfers in suspensions of washed living *Sarcina aurantiaca* but similar suspensions of *S. lutea* failed to support growth. However, *S. lutea* did support growth when supplied as killed suspensions (Johnson, D., 1936). A similar case involves a strain of *Acanthamoeba* which failed to grow on living yeast but grew rather well on autoclaved yeast of the same species (Neff, 1957). Such dietary discretion was not exercised by *Acanthamoeba castellanii*, which grew in cultures with living *Torulopsis famata* or *Candida parapsilosis* and was observed to eat the living yeast cells (Nero, Tarver and Hedrick, 1964). In the case of *Paramecium caudatum* (Johnson, W. H., 1936), *Bacillus subtilis* was the only one of six tested species which supported growth in a non-nutritive salt solution. *Colpoda cucullus*, on the other hand, grew on any one of 27 out of 31 tested species of bacteria Burbanck, 1942).

This use of a single species of microorganisms as a food for a strain of Protozoa — so-called *monoxenic cultures* of Protozoa — has turned out to be a rather useful technique for the maintenance of herbivorous or omnivorous stocks for investigation. Examples include the following: growth of *Allogromia* sp. (Foraminifera) on an unidentified pseudomonad (Lee and Pierce, 1963), *Dictyostelium discoideum* (a cellular slime mold) on *Aerobacter aerogenes* (Sussman, 1961), *Entamoeba invadens* on *Clostridium perfringens* (Balamuth, 1962), *Naegleria gruberi* (a soil amoeba) on *Proteus mirabilis* (Chang, 1958), and a number of earlier examples cited elsewhere (van Wagtendonk, 1955).

Carnivores also have preferred foods. *Didinium nasutum* feeds primarily but not exclusively on some species of *Paramecium*, although it seems to be important that such food organisms are in good health as a result of growth on a suitable bacterial diet (Burbanck and Eisner, 1960). *Bresslaua vorax* thrives on the small ciliate, *Colpoda duodenaria*, but not on the comparable *Tetrahymena pyriformis* (Claff, Dewey, and Kidder, 1941).

Some of the other carnivores are not such fastidious eaters. *Dileptus anser*, for example, can eat a variety of foods under laboratory conditions (Brown and Jenkins, 1962). Various flagellates and ciliates are satisfactory food. Rotifers also may be ingested occasionally. Wounded nematodes and aquatic oligochaetes, small snails and planarian worms, chopped liver, and even fresh clam are eaten with apparent relish by *D. anser*. However, a steady diet of flat worms apparently is not good for *Dileptus* (Janovy, 1963). Feeding on planarians resulted in the appearance of many giants after three or four days. After a week on this diet a few of the giants developed into monsters which eventually became amorphous blobs; some of these blobs divided into several apparently normal ciliates. No such abnormalities were observed in cultures on more nearly normal diets.

## Determination of Minimal Requirements

The minimal requirements of a species are those which are indispensable for growth in serial transfers. The complete identification of such requirements for a freshly captured strain of Protozoa can be a fairly tedious procedure. The first step may be the establishment of a clone, or "pure line," started from a single organism in any medium which will support growth. The next step would be the establishment of an axenic, or bacteria-free, culture in some type of medium which will support growth after sterilization. Bacteria have been eliminated in several ways. Repeated washing in sterile medium and plating out on solid media when possible were popular early methods. More recently, antibiotics and even detergents have occasionally been added to the medium, but there is a possibility that such bacteriostatic or bactericidal substances might produce physiological changes in the Protozoa being isolated. Nevertheless, in the case of some dinoflagellates symbiotic in coelenterates, McLaughlin and Zahl (1959) found it advantageous to start mass bacteria-free cultures with the help of antibiotics and then to use material from these mass cultures for the establishment of clones. The same general procedure has been used previously by Provasoli and his colleagues for isolating many clones of free-living flagellates and algae.

The sterilizable medium for stocks has often contained such things as protein digests (e. g., commercial peptones), salts, and perhaps a sugar, a fatty acid, or sometimes a few added vitamins or other "growth-factors." Such a medium is reproducible and is a dependable source of material for more detailed investigations. The primary aim now becomes replacement of the natural mixtures of amino acids and growth-factors, as represented in commercial peptones and similar materials, by known chemicals supplied in measured quantities. Several, or sometimes many, such mixtures may be tried before the investigator obtains what is wanted, a chemically defined medium which will support adequate growth. Sometimes complications arise. A trace of some natural product, apparently not replaceable by any known growth-factor, has sometimes been necessary for growth in an otherwise chemically defined medium. This situation has been met by attempts to fractionate the natural substance into active and inactive components, in the hope of concentrating and eventually identifying the essential substance. The case of *Tetrahymena pyriformis* and its need for thioctic acid is a good example. Once a medium of known composition has been developed, there remains only one more question. Just which components of this chemically defined medium are actually essential to growth of the species under investigation?

In one procedure, the answer to this question may be sought through a systematic series of deletions designed to strip the original recipe down to bare essentials. This step is not necessarily simple. In complex media for heterotrophs, maintenance of a balance between one amino acid and another can become important (Dewey and Kidder, 1958; Singer, 1961). Furthermore, the presence of a product may "spare" a needed precursor. Once any such complications have been ironed out and the essential foods and growth-factors seem to have been identified, a general safety measure is a test for linear relationships between growth of the organisms and concentrations of the supposedly essential components of the medium. After omission of an essential factor, growth should be reduced to a relatively low level and should fail after the second or third transfer out of a good medium, or sometimes even after the first transfer if there is little carry over from the stock culture.

## Mineral Requirements

Mineral requirements can be highly specific in the case of certain metal ions involved in enzyme activity or electron transport. The investigation of such specific requirements encounters the technical problems of obtaining pure chemicals in the first place and then preventing unrecognized chemical contamination of experimental media. Some of these problems have been discussed in detail (Hutner *et al.*, 1950). If the protozoon under investigation is a heterotroph investigations are particularly complicated because the interpretation of experimental data is not easy. In a general sense, a medium for a heterotroph may be considered a complex system in which various substances, components of the medium, are competing with protozoan enzymes for certain ions. Even if the medium actually contains all the metals needed for growth of the test organism, it might happen that one of the essential metals forms a slightly more stable complex with a component of the medium than it does with its usual enzyme complex. The result could be a metal deficiency severe enough to retard growth of the population.

The addition of a particular metal to such an unfavorable medium may stimulate growth significantly and the stimulation may be proportional, within certain limits, to the amount of metal added. However, it can still be difficult to decide whether the added metal is essential or not. The stimulation may be a direct one if an added essential metal provides an excess over the amount bound by components of the medium. Or, the effect may be indirect if the added metal is a nonessential one which merely displaces some essential metal from its complex with a component of the medium. It may not be easy to determine whether an observed stimulation of growth involves a direct effect or an indirect effect. As an example, Al has been found to stimulate growth of certain flagellates in complex media, but its status as an essential metal is yet to be established.

Failure of growth after omission of a particular metal is not necessarily easy to interpret. An omitted metal ion might have been preventing combination of some essential metal with a component of the medium. If so, removal of this indirectly useful metal might be followed by binding of the essential metal. If the complex is rather stable the observed result could be an inhibition of growth caused by removal of a non-essential metal from the medium.

An effective method for magnifying metal requirements has been revealed by efforts to grow *Ochromonas malhamensis* at temperatures above its usual range. Along with increased requirements for vitamins and metabolites, the flagellates need higher concentrations of copper, manganese and zinc (Hutner, Aaronson, Nathan, Scher, and Cury, 1958).

Both direct and indirect deletion techniques have been followed in attempts to analyze metal requirements of various species. A painstaking procedure was followed in checking *Tetrahymena pyriformis* for a cobalt requirement (Slater, 1952). Solutions of the components of a defined medium were treated with a chelating agent (8-hydroxyquinoline) and the chelator was then removed with chloroform before preparation of the basal medium. A cobalt requirement was apparent in such treated media with no added glucose. Analogous results also have been obtained with *T. pyriformis* by treating a peptone medium with cation exchanger resins and using the filtrate as the basal medium. In serial transfers this medium was inadequate for growth unless supplemented with magnesium. Several other metals, some of which have been reported as substitutes for magnesium in activation of certain enzymes, supported no growth beyond the first transfer, but with a magnesium supplement vigorous growth was maintained through six serial transfers (Hall, 1954). Such omission techniques have been used extensively by Provasoli and his colleagues in developing media for various phytoflagellates and algae.

Indirect deletion, by addition of a chelating agent directly to the experimental medium, has been tried in some work on heterotrophs. Oxalate and citrate have been used with *T. pyriformis*, reversal being obtained by addition of magnesium. Inhibition of growth by addition of hemoglobin to cultures of *Euglena gracilis* has been interpreted (Coelho and Reye, 1963) as the inhibitory effect of a chelating agent (probably the globin portion of hemoglobin). Such an interpretation is supported by the reversal evident upon addition of calcium to the medium containing hemoglobin. The reversing effect of magnesium or manganese was much less striking than that of calcium. More or less similar reversals have been reported for *Tetrahymena* with EDTA as the chelating agent. Interpretation of results in such cases depends upon the relative stabilities of the various metal-complexes formed with the chelating agent. A nonessential metal which forms highly stable EDTA complexes will displace a bound metal from a less stable complex, for example. Hence, it is possible for the addition of a nonessential metal to a chelated medium to insure growth of a test organism by freeing a previously bound metal (an essential one) from its EDTA complex (Hall, 1954a).

An important application of chelating agents is their use in creating a metal "buffering system" in experimental media. This technique, utilized with much success by Provasoli and his colleagues (Provasoli, McLaughlin, and Droop, 1957; Provasoli and Pintner, 1960) permits addition of metals in otherwise potentially toxic excess. With appropriate concentrations of metals and chelating agents, slow dissociation of the complexes maintains a necessary concentration of metals without endangering survival of the organisms. The method has worked even with some of the most sensitive species tested so far, although one chelating agent may be more satisfactory than another for a particular species. This type of metal buffering also has made possible growth of certain flagellates (*Euglena gracilis*, *Ochromonas malhamensis*) at high temperatures — that is, temperatures above the normal biothermal range (Hutner, Baker, Aaronson, etc., 1957).

There are additional complications in analyzing the mineral requirements of marine and brackish water species. The concentration of certain salts (especially NaCl and certain magnesium salts) is important in maintenance of a favorable salinity (Provasoli and McLaughlin, 1963). The optimal salinity may vary from species to species. Some marine flagellates, such as *Exuviella cassubica*, can grow in a rather wide range of salinities (0.08–3.8 per cent salinity) extending to those of brackish waters; others, such as *Rhodomonas lens*, are restricted to conditions approaching those of seawater more closely (Provasoli, McLaughlin, and Pintner, 1954). For *Peridinium balticum*, a brackish water species, a salinity of 0.8–1.2 per cent is optimal for growth; for some of the other dinoflagellates, the optimum is 2.0–2.5 per cent salinity (Provasoli and McLaughlin, 1963). In addition to salinity, such factors as the Ca/Mg ratio and the monovalent/divalent ion ratio have been considered in the development of media for marine species (Provasoli, 1958; Provasoli, McLaughlin, and Droop, 1957). Such media are not really attempts to duplicate natural seawater. Instead, they are carefully developed substitutes with a chelating agent added and the calcium content reduced to a minimum to help avoid undesirable precipitates. In addition, the salinity is often lower than that of natural seawater, except for media used in special cases. Trace metals are added with suitable amounts of a chelating agent (such as a sodium salt of EDTA, nitrilotriacetic acid or hydroxyethyl-ethylenediaminetriacetic acid) to establish a metal-buffering system. A representative medium, medium ASP 2 of Provasoli, McLaughlin and Droop (1957), is satisfactory for a number of marine Chrysomonadida, Cryptomonadida and Dinoflagellida, as well as some of the diatoms, blue-green algae and green algae (Table 1).

Media of this general type have been modified for different species by changing the concentration of particular trace metals, adding an amino acid or so or some other organic enrichments, or else increasing the salinity (by increasing NaCl content especially and that of $MgSO_4$ to a smaller extent). Such media of higher salinity have been applied successfully to growth of several marine dinoflagellates and chrysomonads (McLaughlin, Zahl, Nowack, Marchisotto and Prager, 1960). So far, these investigations with chemically defined substitutes for seawater have produced axenic cultures of several chrysomonads, at least one of the Silicoflagellida, a number of Dinoflagellida, and a few Cryptomonadida, as well as various diatoms and other algae. Such media are being tried also in attempts to establish axenic cultures of various Foraminifera (Lee *et al.*, 1963; Lee and Pierce, 1963).

Very little is known about the uptake of minerals from the medium, although available data indicate that different methods may be involved for different metals. In *Acanthamoeba*, for example, uptake of K proceeds against a concentration gradient, whereas the internal and external concentrations of Na tend to become equalized (Klein, 1961). In terms of environmental content, the utilization of particular minerals often involves a very striking concentration of the substance inside the organism. According to data cited by Provasoli (1958), this concentration factor

TABLE 1

Synthetic Medium for Marine Flagellates and Algae
(medium ASP 2 of Provasoli, McLaughlin, and Droop)

| | |
|---|---|
| NaCl | 1.8 g |
| $MgSO_4$ | 0.5 g |
| KCl | 0.06 g |
| Ca (as chloride) | 10.0 mg |
| $NaNO_3$ | 5.0 mg |
| $KH_2PO_4$ | 0.5 mg |
| $NaSiO_3.9H_2O$ | 15.0 mg |
| Buffer ("Tris") | 100.0 mg |
| Vitamin $B_{12}$ | 0.2 $\mu$g |
| Thiamine-HCl | 50.0 $\mu$g |
| Nicotinic acid | 10.0 $\mu$g |
| Ca-pantothenate | 10.0 $\mu$g |
| *p*-aminobenzoic acid | 1.0 $\mu$g |
| Biotin | 0.1 $\mu$g |
| Inositol | 0.5 $\mu$g |
| Folic acid | 0.2 $\mu$g |
| Thymine | 0.3 mg |
| Trace metals: | |
| $\quad$ $Na_3$-EDTA | 3.0 mg |
| $\quad$ Fe  (as $Cl^-$) | 0.08 mg |
| $\quad$ Zn  (as $Cl^-$) | 15.0 $\mu$g |
| $\quad$ Mn (as $Cl^-$) | 0.12 mg |
| $\quad$ Co  (as $Cl^-$) | 0.3 $\mu$g |
| $\quad$ Cu  (as $Cl^-$) | 0.12 $\mu$g |
| $\quad$ B    (as $H_3BO_3$) | 0.6 mg |
| Distilled water | 100.0 ml |

for phosphorus reaches 100,000–300,000 times in such flagellates as
*Euglena, Pandorina* and *Volvox*. Metals required by one species or another
apparently include the following: calcium, cobalt, copper, iron, magnesium, manganese, molybdenum, phosphorus, potassium, silicon, strontium, sulfur, vanadium and zinc. There is no assurance that all protozoan
species need every listed metal. Furthermore, there is no assurance that
this list is complete, in view of the technical difficulties complicating
investigations of metal requirements. Other possibilities include alumi-
num, barium, boron, iodine and sodium, each of which has been found

to stimulate growth of one or more species, at least under particular experimental conditions.

Although there may be some uncertainty about various qualitative requirements, it is obvious that the quantitative requirement for a metal may vary from species to species. Calcium is a good example. Among the Sarcodina, for instance, the foraminiferan test is commonly a calcareous one, the calcite (in the majority of living genera) being deposited in an organic matrix which may retain its characteristic form after decalcification (Bé and Ericson, 1963). Calcium is utilized in unusual amounts also by those Chrysomonadida which bear calcareous coccoliths. In *Hymenomonas*, for example, these structures are produced in the cytoplasm and later passed to the surface, formation of coccoliths being dependent upon a satisfactory concentration of calcium in the medium (Isenberg *et al.*, 1963a). Intracytoplasmic formation of coccoliths also has been reported in *Coccolithus huxleyi* and there seems to be no evidence that these skeletal structures can be produced or even increased in size at the body surface (Wilbur and Wanatabe, 1963). In *C. huxleyi*, calcification occurs in an organic matrix which presumably influences the form of each developing coccolith.

The production of coccoliths in *Hymenomonas* sp. has been inhibited by a carbonic anhydrase inhibitor (2-acetylamino-1,3,4-thiadiazole-5-sulfonamide). As a result, it was suggested that under normal conditions carbonic anhydrase may liberate from excess catabolic bicarbonate a supply of carbonate which combines with calcium ions on the organic matrix involved in formation of coccoliths (Isenberg *et al.*, 1963).

Calcium, along with magnesium ions, also has turned up among the several factors inducing encystment of *Hartmanella rhysodes* in a defined medium (Band, 1963). A relationship of metal ions to the life cycle likewise has been reported for *Naegleria gruberi* (Willner, 1956). Extra Mg ions, and Na to a lesser degree, prevent metamorphosis of *N. gruberi* from the amoeba to the flagellate stage. The inhibition does not involve osmotic pressure as such. The presence of both calcium and magnesium ions seems to be necessary for the mating type reaction (flagellar agglutination) in heterothallic chlamydomonad flagellates (Wiese and Jones, 1963). Unusual needs for silicon are characteristic of most Radiolaria and also of the Silicoflagellida since both groups build siliceous skeletons. Similarly, the Acantharia (Actipylea) build their skeletal elements with strontium sulfate as a substitute for silicon compounds.

**Nitrogenous Foods**

Under natural conditions the nitrogenous foods of Protozoa as a group include a wide variety of substances. These range in complexity from inorganic salts dissolved in water to the constituent proteins of other microorganisms or small Metazoa. However, the types of food adequate for growth vary considerably in different groups of Protozoa. As might be expected, the phytoflagellates include many forms which can get along on an inorganic compound as the only source of nitrogen. The rest of the Protozoa must have more complex nitrogenous foods because their biosynthetic abilities are less extensive than those of the phytoflagellates.

Although some microorganisms can assimilate atmospheric nitrogen and others can grow on a nitrite, there is no evidence that any protozoon can use either free nitrogen or a nitrite as the sole nitrogen source. Ammonium salts and nitrates are the inorganic sources which remain available. Of these, a nitrate can be used by many but not by all of the chlorophyll-bearing flagellates and also by a very few colorless phytoflagellates, such as the phytomonad *Polytomella ocellatum*. More typically, a colorless flagellate cannot grow on a nitrate even though the species can grow well on an ammonium salt. The basic metabolic deficiency responsible for this handicap has not yet been identified, although utilization of a nitrate obviously would demand reduction as a preliminary step in utilization. Even some of the green flagellates, such as *Euglena gracilis* (Birdsey and Lynch, 1962), cannot grow on nitrate as the nitrogen source, in spite of the fact that *E. gracilis* can reduce nitrate to nitrite. Other chlorophyll – bearing flagellates, such as dinoflagellates belonging to at least five genera (Provasoli and McLaughlin, 1963), can thrive on a nitrate. In fact, Provasoli (1958) concluded that the majority of green flagellates can use either a nitrate or an ammonium salt. However, an ammonium salt is utilized more commonly because so many colorless species cannot grow on nitrates. In media containing both types of nitrogen sources, the ammonium salt is utilized first by species which have been tested (Provasoli, 1958). In laboratory cultures of suitable flagellates a nitrate is often preferred by investigators because its utilization does not lead to a drop in pH of a lightly buffered medium for a freshwater species. When media are used at a pH below

7.0, however, an ammonium salt is a good nitrogen source (McLaughlin, 1958). If media are alkaline, ammonium salts are more apt to be toxic for such susceptible species as *Prymnesium parvum*. This "ammonia effect" has been applied to the control of *P. parvum* during blooms of the flagellates in fish ponds in Israel. At fairly low concentrations (0.5 mg/100 ml, or less), however, ammonium chloride is satisfactory for a variety of dinoflagellates and chrysomonads at pH levels up to 7.8–7.9 (McLaughlin *et al.*, 1960). Such data indicate clearly that, under natural conditions, flagellates are rarely in danger of being poisoned by high concentrations of ammonium salts. Theoretically, of course, such toxicity might be encountered in unusual environments characterized by heavy pollution with organic material, including much protein undergoing decomposition with liberation of ammonia.

As for organic sources of nitrogen, the ability to use one or more such foods may be more or less universal in Protozoa. However, it appears that at least some of the phytoflagellates can use this type of food primarily as a source of ammonia. Cirillo's tests with *Chilomonas paramecium*, a colorless cryptomonad flagellate, showed that only two amino acids and two amides approached an ammonium salt in effectiveness as a sole nitrogen source. Much like an ammonium salt for *Chilomonas*, a nitrate was just as good a nitrogen source as any of the amino acids tested for a number of different dinoflagellates (Provasoli and McLaughlin, 1963).

A few of the phytoflagellates are exceptional in that specific requirements for one or more amino acids have been developed. For example, the unusual phagotrophic euglenoid, *Peranema trichophorum*, must have both methionine and tryptophan as supplements to the medium (Hutner and Provasoli, 1955). Such requirements indicate that this flagellate has lost the ability to synthesize these amino acids, an ability still retained by various related euglenoid flagellates.

Some of the apparent differences in availability of amino acids may depend either upon ability to take up individual amino acids from the culture medium or upon differences in enzymatic equipment needed for their use in metabolism. The rate of uptake may differ from one species to another, as demonstrated for glycine in *Amoeba proteus* and a ciliate, *Stentor coeruleus* (Chadwick, 1961). This amino acid is taken up very slowly by *A. proteus* unless pinocytosis is evoked by adding an inducer to the medium. The ciliate, on the other hand, takes up glycine rather rapidly. Such differences in rate of uptake may exist also among phyto-flagellates, and it is likely that the rate of uptake varies significantly with different amino acids.

Outside the group of phytoflagellates, however, requirements for specific amino acids are to be expected. A strain of *Crithidia oncopelti* represents an exceptional case in that methionine is the only required amino acid in a defined medium (Newton, 1957). This odd situation is perhaps to be correlated with a bacterial infection, the parasite (or, more accurately, symbiote) presumably being responsible for synthesis of various amino acids required by related heterotrophs (Gill and Vogel, 1963). In this case, it is not surprising to learn that synthesis of lysine in *C. oncopelti* involves a series of reactions which are characteristic of bacteria and various other plants but not of animals (Vogel, 1959): diaminopomelic acid appears as an intermediate.

Heterotrophs in general have nitrogen requirements much more com-plex than those of *Crithidia oncopelti* with its endoparasitic bacteria. Excepting such cases of symbiosis, it is a reasonably safe assumption that a single amino acid is never an adequate source of nitrogen for heterotrophs outside the phytoflagellates. However, there is a fairly wide range in the abilities of such organisms to synthesize amino acids or, conversely, in their requirements for specific amino acids. Representative heterotrophs with specific amino acid requirements are listed in Table 2. One of the small amoebae, *Hartmanella rhysodes*, is able to synthesize all except seven of its constituent amino acids (Band, 1962). A related species, *Acanthamoeba* sp., can synthesize all except arginine, isoleucine, leucine, methionine, phenylalanine and valine, but needs supplementary glycine in addition for vigorous growth (Adam, 1964). The ciliate, *Tetrahymena pyriformis*, can synthesize all except ten or eleven of its amino acids; certain strains, unlike others, lack the inherited ability to synthesize serine (Elliott and Clark, 1958a). One of the trypanosomid flagellates, *Crithidia fasciculata*, can synthesize all except ten of its amino acids (Cowperthwaite *et al.*, 1953) but the related *Leishmania tarentolae* (Trager, 1957a) is unable to synthesize at least fifteen of the amino acids listed in Table 2. Among the investigated species of *Tetrahymena*, minor differences in ability to synthesize amino acids have been noted. Also, *Paramecium multimicronucleatum*, in contrast to *T. pyriformis*, is unable to synthesize thirteen of its amino acids (Johnson and Miller, 1957). Perhaps the most common disabilities in synthesis involve the following

TABLE 2
Amino Acids Required by Several Heterotrophs

| Amino acid | Acantha-moeba | H. rhy-sodes | L. taren-tolae[4] | T. pyri-formis | G. chat-toni |
|---|---|---|---|---|---|
| Arginine | + | + | + | + | + |
| Glycine[1] | + | − | − | − | |
| Histidine | − | − | + | + | + |
| Isoleucine | + | + | + | + | + |
| Leucine | + | + | + | + | + |
| Lysine | − | + | + | + | + |
| Methionine | + | + | + | + | + |
| Phenylalanine | + | − | + | + | + |
| Proline[2] | − | − | + | − | + |
| Serine[3] | | − | + | + | + |
| Threonine[1] | | + | + | + | + |
| Tryptophan | − | − | + | + | + |
| Tyrosine | + | − | + | − | − |
| Valine | + | + | + | + | + |

[1]Glycine replaces serine, or *vice versa*, in *Acanthamoeba* and *G. chattoni;* in the former, threonine also replaces glycine fairly well. [2]Proline is an imino acid. [3]In *Tetrahymena*, needed by rare strains showing mendelian inheritance of the requirement. [4]Additional amino acids (alanine, aspartate, glutamate, glycine) have been supplied for better growth.

amino acids: arginine, isoleucine, leucine, lysine, methionine, threonine and valine. Tryptophan, histidine and phenylalanine also are commonly involved in biosynthetic deficiencies.

The question of the adequacy of artificial mixtures of amino acids has interested some workers. It was even concluded in one case (Kidder, Dewey, and Fuller, 1954) that such ciliates as *Colpidium campylum* and *Glaucoma chattoni* (= "*G. scintillans*") must have more complex nitrogenous foods (polypeptides) for growth in laboratory cultures. This conclusion is negated by the more recent demonstration that *G. chattoni* grows well on a mixture of twelve amino acids plus appropriate growth factors (Holz *et al.*, 1961).

Outside the laboratory, heterotrophic Protozoa must usually rely upon proteins in the small organisms they ingest or else upon decomposition products of plants and animals. Phagotrophs often depend heavily upon microorganisms they eat, and these eaters digest such foods with appropriate proteinases and peptidases for the nitrogenous components. In laboratory tests, digestion of casein, fibrinogen, gelatin and hemoglobin has been reported for various phagotrophs, especially ciliates. Some of the hemoglobin eaters are malarial parasites, for which this substance represents probably the major source of food. Cooking, as in autoclave sterilization, facilitates digestion of egg albumin, hemoglobin, serum albumin and soy protein by *Tetrahymena pyriformis*. Tests with extracts containing proteinases of malarial parasites and *T. pyriformis* have indicated maximal activity at pH 6.0–6.5, intermediate between optima for pepsins and trypsins of higher animals. Proteolytic activity also has been reported for such nonphagocytic organisms as *Leishmania tropica* and *Euglena gracilis* but the origin of such enzymes in the medium remains uncertain. The possibility that such enzymes reach the external medium after disintegration of some of the organisms has not been eliminated. Furthermore, some of the supposedly saprozoic protein-digesters may not be exclusively saprozoic after all. The demonstration that malarial parasites ingest cytoplasm of the invaded red corpuscle and the description of a cytostome and gullet in the "saprozoic" *Trypanosoma mega* raise obvious questions about some of the other supposedly saprozoic organisms which can digest natural proteins.

No matter how a species actually obtains its nitrogenous food or what the chemical or physical form in which this food is available, the ultimate aim of the protozoon is synthesis of those proteins which make up the enzymes and structural components of the organism. For microorganisms in general, the key nitrogen compound in synthesis of amino acids is ammonia which can be converted into amino or amide groups. So far as Protozoa are concerned, potential sources are ammonium salts, nitrates, amino acids, or peptides and natural proteins. It may be assumed that, aside from the species which require one or more specific amino acids, phytoflagellates use any such nitrogen source primarily as a source of ammonia for use in biosynthesis. Such a synthesis may involve amination (catalyzed by glutamic deaminase) of an α-ketodicarboxylic acid (α-ketoglutaric acid) which is readily available in aerobes from the TCA pool. The result is glumatic acid. Another primary pathway involves the amination of fumaric acid, also from the TCA pool, by aspartase (aspartic deaminase) to produce aspartic acid. These two primary amino acids may serve as donors of amino groups in transaminations involving various keto acids and resulting in a number of additional amino acids. Alanine, for example, may be synthesized from glumatic and pyruvic acids, leucine from glutamic and α-ketoisocaproic acid, and so on. Amino acids also may contribute carbon chains in synthesis of other amino acids. In *Crithidia oncopelti* (Newton, 1957), for example, either glutamic acid or aspartic acid, labeled with $C^{14}$, was utilized for synthesis of at least twelve other amino acids. Some of the amino acids are synthesized by methods which do not directly involve transamination of an $\alpha$-keto acid with aspartic or glutamic acid. Tryptophan, for example, is formed by a condensation of serine and indole in certain microorganisms. In one way or another, an organism equipped with the appropriate enzymes and supplied with the necessary substrates can synthesize all its protoplasmic amino acids. Species with one or more deficiencies in enzymatic equipment must have a ready made supply of the amino acids which the organisms cannot synthesize. Once the needed amino acids have been taken in or synthesized, the organism is able to build its supply of proteins needed for growth and reproduction.

The amino acids which cannot be synthesized by a species are its so-called *essential amino acids*, the ones the species must obtain from external sources. In laboratory cultures, it has been possible to grow certain species in media containing these essential amino acids and no others. In such a case, a heterotroph obviously has to build its nonessential amino acids from the available supply of essential ones. The identity of such doubly useful amino acids has been determined for *Tetrahymena pyriformis* (Wu and Hogg, 1952). Ciliates fed only the eleven amino acids needed by strain E of *T. pyriformis* were shown, by analytical techniques, to depend upon a group of five essential amino acids as substrates for synthesis of nonessential amino acids. These five were arginine, methionine, serine, threonine, and tryptophan. Five of the remaining amino acids supplied to the ciliates apparently were incorporated directly into proteins of the organisms. Histidine, for reasons not determined, was needed in much greater amount than that actually assimilated. In contrast to *T. pyriformis*, arginine was assimilated mainly as such by *Crithidia oncopelti*, with little or no interconversion (Newton, 1957).

In addition to proteins, Protozoa must synthesize nucleic acids and various types of coenzymes. Synthesis of nucleic acids requires a supply of purines and pyrimidines. Phytoflagellates typically can synthesize both types of bases from the components of relatively simple media. *Acanthamoeba* sp. seems to possess a comparable ability to synthesize both purines and pyrimidines from nonspecific precursors (Adam, 1959), although from less simple substrates. Some of the other Protozoa are less independent. Certain species must start with the purine ring in synthesis of their nucleic acid purines. Others need not only a purine but also a pyrimidine as starting points in biosynthesis. Such organisms as *Crithidia fasciculata*, even though they lack the ability to build the purine ring, can start their syntheses with any one of the natural purines, or else their ribosides or nucleotides (Aaronson and Nathan, 1954) and even an analogue, 2, 6-diamino-purine (Kidder and Dutta, 1958). The chrysomonad flagellate, *Ochromonas malhamensis*, also has a somewhat limited ability to synthesize its nucleic-acid purines from this analogue (Hamilton, 1953). Ciliates seem to be more exacting in their requirements. *Tetrahymena pyriformis* and *Glaucoma chattoni* can use guanine as a source of nucleic-acid guanine and adenine, but adenine does not serve the same purpose as a substrate. Dietary $C^{14}$-adenine is used for producing nucleic-acid adenine only. Certain ciliates use a derivative of guanine more effectively than the base itself; guanylic acid is better for *Tetrahymena corlissi* and *T. paravorax*, for example. *Paramecium multimicronucleatum* also uses guanylic acid, as well as the riboside (guanosine), whereas guanine itself is inadequate.

Inability to synthesize pyrimidines seems to be less common than a purine deficiency in Protozoa. *Crithidia fasciculata*, for instance, can grow without a pyrimidine in the medium even though it does need a dietary purine. *Tetrahymena pyriformis*, on the other hand, shows a pyrimidine requirement which can be satisfied by supplementary uracil (or uridine, or uridylic acid) or cytidine (or cytidylic acid). Also, *T. corlissi*, *T. paravorax* and *T. setifera* (Holz *et al.*, 1962) can use uracil for synthesizing their pyrimidines. *Paramecium multimicronucleatum*, however, needs either the riboside or nucleotide derivative of cytosine or uracil rather than either base (Johnson and Miller, 1957). It is possible, of course, that differences in rates of uptake rather than in enzymatic deficiencies in biosynthesis proper may be involved in some of these differences in purine and pyrimidine requirements involving the bases and their derivatives.

## Carbon Sources

Although carbon sources vary to some extent with the species or larger group of Protozoa, assimilation of carbon dioxide is probably a general feature in spite of the fact that the process has been traced in only a few species so far. As a sole carbon source, carbon dioxide is adequate for a number of representative chlorophyll-bearing flagellates if they are maintained in light. Such species as *Chlamydomonas agloeformis*, *C. reinhardi* and *Chlorogonium elongatum* are good examples. Although some of the chlorophyll-bearing flagellates, such as *Euglena gracilis*, can oxidize carbon monoxide to carbon dioxide, it is still uncertain that the monoxide can serve as the sole carbon source for phototrophic species. Some of the phytoflagellates seem to be more or less restricted to carbon dioxide as a carbon source in light. *Gymnodinium breve* apparently is a good representative of such "photoautotrophic" organisms (Aldrich, 1962). Addition of any one of twenty carbohydrates, seven alcohols, nine fatty acids, and thirteen intermediates of the TCA cycle and glycolytic pathway to a basal medium, which had already been found inadequate for survival or reproduction of *G. breve* in darkness, revealed no useful carbon source among the compounds tested. Even such things as casein hydrolysates and soil extracts proved useless in darkness. In addition, incubation of cultures in light in a $CO_2$-free atmosphere prevented reproduction and survival of already established cultures. The available data obviously seem to qualify *G. breve* as an obligate phototroph, with no tendency toward heterotrophy other than requirements for three vitamins. *Euglena gracilis*, although chlorophyll-bearing, is a facultative heterotroph which grows fairly well in darkness in a suitable medium. In such a good medium, *E. gracilis* has shown little sensitivity to changes in light intensities. Under comparable conditions, *Chlamydomonas moewusii* was quite sensitive to differences in light intensity, failing to grow at all when the intensity was less than 15 ft-c (Gross and Jahn, 1962). However, when *E. gracilis* is placed in a medium which demands phototrophy for survival and reproduction, growth of the flagellate population is markedly influenced by intensity of light (Cook, 1963).

Although assimilation of carbon dioxide has been traced in both the chlorophyll-bearing *E. gracilis* (Lynch and Calvin, 1953) and in representative heterotrophs, a ciliate (*Tetrahymena pyriformis*) and one of the Mycetozoa (*Physarum polycephalum*), the biochemical pathways are not the same in all three cases. In the two heterotrophs, labeled carbon of the assimilated $CO_2$ was traced into intermediates of the tricarboxylic acid cycle (TCA cycle), a type of assimilation characteristic of animals. In *T. pyriformis* it is reported that assimilation of $CO_2$ is mediated by phosphoenolpyruvic carboxykinase (Warnock and van Eys, 1962). In representative green algae (*Chlorella, Scendesmus*), carbon dioxide is assimilated into phosphorylated carbohydrates and their precursors in the presence of light. This pathway is characteristic of photosynthetic organisms. *Euglena gracilis* apparently combines the photosynthetic and the animal pathways with an ability to carry on a $CO_2$-fixation of the photosynthetic type in darkness. This biochemical versatility seems appropriate for an organism often assumed to resemble the stage at which the ancestral plant-animals split up into two distinct stocks, primitive plants and animals. Modern plants have retained the photosynthetic pathway while animals follow the animal type of fixation.

All typical heterotrophs, as well as green species which can be maintained in darkness, must have a carbon source less simple than carbon dioxide. The green phytoflagellates, under such conditions, need an organic compound as a source of energy since they can no longer depend upon photosynthesis. Heterotrophic Protozoa have always had this problem. Carbon sources vary considerably in their suitability for particular species, but the range in chemical complexity, for Protozoa as a whole, is wide — from a 2-carbon fatty acid on up to a polysaccharide. Adequacy of any particular carbon source depends upon several factors. In the first place, the substance must get into the body of the organism in one way or another. Then, if uptake has been possible, the organism must be able to attack the carbon source enzymatically in such a way that energy becomes available for metabolism. It is helpful also if the carbon source yields a product or two which the consumer can use in synthesis.

An interesting side effect of a good carbon source, ethanol, on *Euglena gracilis* indicates that a perfectly useful food can be a mixed blessing under unusual circumstances. When *E. gracilis* was kept in darkness for a week or so and then returned to light, suspended in a salt solution which does not support reproduction, exposure to ethanol suppressed both the synthesis of chlorophyll and the production of hexose-diphosphatase (App and Jagendorf, 1963).

Of all the organic carbon sources tested, acetate seems to be one of the most favorable for phytoflagellates, many of which have been referred to as "acetate flagellates." Acetate, in fact, was the only one of several tested substrates which supported growth of *Chlamydomonas reinhardi* in darkness (Sager and Granick, 1953). On the other hand, *C. dysmosos* has grown in darkness with acetate, lactate or pyruvate as the energy source in a mineral medium (Lewin, 1954). Such differences may not depend entirely upon the specific carbon source, since *Chilomonas paramecium* failed to grow on pyruvate as the carbon source unless the medium contained thiamine, while acetate supported very slow but transplantable growth without supplementary thiamine (Cosgrove, 1950). An analogous situation has turned up in *Polytomella caeca*, which needs much larger supplements of thiamine as the concentration of alcoholic substrate is increased (Wise *et al.*, 1961).

*Euglena gracilis* utilizes acetate a little more efficiently than ethanol (Wilson and Danforth, 1958) — an efficiency of 42 per cent, only slightly better than that earlier reported for *Chilomonas paramecium*. *E. gracilis* apparently assimilates acetate by incorporation into TCA-cycle oxalacetic acid, as indicated by experiments with carboxyl- and methyl-labeled materials (Danforth, 1961).

Among the Sarcodina, growth of *Acanthamoeba* sp. is stimulated by acetate (Adam, 1959), the rate of growth being independent of the acetate concentration within the range tested (0.05–0.25 g/100 ml). The data seemed to indicate that the undissociated acetate molecule enters the amoeba rather readily, in contrast to glucose which seems to be taken in largely by pinocytosis (Chapman-Andresen and Holter, 1955). Acetate is utilized also by various other Protozoa outside the group of phytoflagellates. Assimilation of $C^{14}$-acetate into amino acids and pyrimidines has been reported for *Crithidia oncopelti* (Newton, 1957), and a stimulatory effect of acetate in a moderately satisfactory medium has been observed previously in *Tetrahymena pyriformis*. The presence of acetate in the medium also has been found to reduce the requirement of *T. pyriformis* for thioctic acid, although acetate cannot replace the growthfactor. In view of the effects reported for *Acanthamoeba* and *Tetrahymena*, it is probable that acetate can be used readily by a number of other heterotrophs as well as by many colorless phytoflagellates.

In addition to acetate, certain other organic acids are used by phytoflagellates (Table 3). A fairly wide variety of carbon sources is suitable for some species. *Chilomonas paramecium* (Holz, 1954), for example, can use as major carbon sources at least three alcohols and ten organic acids; *Polytomella caeca* (Wise, 1959), seven acids and four alcohols. These two species, members of different orders of phytoflagellates, differ in their ability to use certain specific carbon sources. Thus, caproic,

TABLE 3
Carbon Sources Adequate for Several Phytoflagellates

| Acids, alcohols | C. para-mecium | P. caeca | E. gra-cilis | Astasia longa |
|---|---|---|---|---|
| n-butyric | + | + | + | + |
| n-caproic | + | − | + | + |
| n-caprylic | + | − | | |
| Fumaric | + | − | | |
| α-ketoglutarate | + | | | |
| Lactic | + | − | | ± |
| Malic | + | | | ± |
| Propionic | | + | + | |
| Pyruvic | + | + | | |
| Succinic | + | + | | ± |
| Valeric | | + | + | + |
| n-butanol | + | + | + | + |
| Ethanol | + | + | + | + |
| Hexanol | + | + | | + |
| n-propanol | | + | | + |

+Good carbon source;   ±, fairly good utilization;   −, inadequate.

caprylic, fumaric and lactic acids, all of which have supported growth of *C. paramecium*, are inadequate as major carbon sources for *P. caeca*. However, homogenates of *P. caeca* reduced methylene blue in the presence of either lactic or fumaric acid, indicating that at least some of the observed interspecific differences may depend upon problems of uptake rather than the presence or absence of enzymes capable of attacking particular substrates. Some of the other "carbon-source disabilities" reported in phytoflagellates may involve similar situations. Intermediates of the TCA cycle are a good example. Failure to detect stimulation of growth by such substrates has been reported for intact flagellates in several cases. Homogenates of *Euglena gracilis* (a bleached strain), on the other hand, have oxidized at least six TCA acids (Danforth, 1953), thus extending the comparable results reported for four of them in homogenates of *P. caeca*. In testing such carbon sources, the pH of the medium can have an important influence on the observed results. *Polytomella caeca* used succinate most efficiently at pH 3.0 and pyruvate at pH 4.0 (Wise, 1959). These pH levels are well below those in which such carbon sources have been tested in some cases. This relation of pH of the medium to utilization of substrates, as well as a specificity of carbon sources which does not depend upon oxidative enzymes, and also the independence of growth stimulation and amount of substrate above a certain concentration, were responsible for the suggestion (Wise, 1959) that uptake of acid carbon sources may involve a sort of "coenzyme-A pump" analogous to the hexosephosphate uptake mechanism reported in various other microorganisms.

Utilization of seven TCA-cycle intermediates has been reported for *Tetrahymena pyriformis*, and oxidation of most of these acids has been demonstrated also in several species of *Plasmodium*. Differences have been noted in various trichomonad flagellates. Thus, *T. gallinae* can oxidize six TCA-cycle intermediates, while *T. vaginalis* has shown no activity for them. Such trypanosomes as *T. cruzi* can oxidize at least certain of the dicarboxylic acids. Occasional negative reports for intact trypanosomes of various species may be attributable in part to the failure of tested substrates to penetrate the flagellates under particular experimental conditions.

Although certain carbohydrates are excellent carbon sources for those species which can use them, not all Protozoa are so constructed or equipped as to realize the potential benefits of carbohydrates as food. Many phytoflagellates belong in this less fortunate group. Examples are some of the dinoflagellates, the cryptomonad *Chilomonas*, some of the phytomonads, and various Euglenida. Certain exceptions are known among the Euglenida — e.g., a mutant strain of *Astasia longa* (differing from the parent stock, which does not use glucose), *Euglena gracilis* var. *bacillaris* — and may exist also in some of the other orders. The Chrysomonadida, as represented by *Ochromonas*, have no particular difficulty in consuming carbohydrates. *Ochromonas malhamensis* can digest starch, and also uses sucrose and several monosaccharides. Of course, *Ochromonas* is an unusual phytoflagellate in some respects, chlorophyll-bearing but in spite of it perhaps more of a heterotroph than a phototrophic organism. Some protozoologists have even questioned the ability of *O. malhamensis* to survive if it were forced to depend on photosynthesis alone for its energy.

Outside the group of phytoflagellates, Protozoa in general favor carbohydrates as sources of energy and carbon chains. However, the relative usefulness of a particular carbohydrate may vary with the species. Thus, *Crithidia oncopelti* uses lactic acid and succinic acid more readily than it does galactose and several disaccharides, although glucose is perhaps the most satisfactory energy source for this species. This trypanosomid flagellate differs from many phytoflagellates in that acetate is not particularly suitable and is by no means a good substitute for glucose. *Trichomonas foetus*, like *Crithidia*, uses both lactic and pyruvic acids almost as readily as glucose (Doran, 1957). Differences in utilization of particular carbohydrates are well known among Protozoa (Table 4).

TABLE 4
Carbohydrates Utilized by Several Heterotrophs

| Carbohydrate | T. foe-tus | T. gal-linae | L. trop-ica | T. pyrifor-mis |
|---|---|---|---|---|
| Arabinose | − | + | − | − |
| Cellobiose | | | | +* |
| Dextrin | + | | − | + |
| Fructose | + | + | + | + |
| Fucose | | | | − |
| Galactose | + | + | + | +* |
| Glucose | + | + | + | + |
| Glycogen | | + | | +* |
| Inulin | + | | + | +* |
| Lactose | + | | | − |
| Lyxose | | | | − |
| Maltose | + | + | ± | + |
| Mannose | | | + | + |
| Melizitose | | | | − |
| Raffinose | + | | + | − |
| Rhamnose | − | | | − |
| Ribose | | | | − |
| Starch | | + | | + |
| Sucrose | + | + | + | − |
| Trehalose | | + | | |
| Turanose | | + | | |
| Xylose | − | | − | − |

*Reported for certain strains.

Although starch is used by many phagotrophic Protozoa, the ability to digest some of the other polysaccharides apparently is not so widespread. In all these cases, digestion of the carbohydrate is an essential preliminary step and the appropriate carbohydrases evidently are not universally distributed among phagotrophs. The presence of cellulases is to be assumed in those phagotrophs which normally feed largely on algae and likewise in certain parasites which invade the cells of higher plants. Specific laboratory tests for cellulase activity have been positive for certain flagellates from wood-eating termites and the wood roach and also for certain rumen ciliates (*e.g.*, *Diplodinium* spp.). In addition, cellulase activity has been determined for such free-living ciliates as *Paramecium caudatum* and *Chilodonella cucullus*.

Tested strains of *Tetrahymena pyriformis* have shown the ability to digest starch and dextrin, but the ability to digest inulin seems to vary from one strain to another, or even from one laboratory to another. Tests on malarial parasites have been negative for enzymes capable of digesting polysaccharides, although this should not be especially surprising in view of the normal diet of these organisms.

The ability to use disaccharides is rather common in both free-living and parasitic Protozoa, but the utilization of a particular sugar may vary from one species to another. Among the ciliates, *Colpidium campylum* uses sucrose, as do various trypanosomid and trichomonad flagellates. Several strains of *Tetrahymena pyriformis*, on the other hand, find sucrose useless, and so does *Glaucoma chattoni*. Maltose, however, can be used by a number of ciliates and also by some of the parasitic flagellates, but lactose seems to be useless for these same ciliates although it serves as food for those flagellates which can utilize maltose.

Except for glucose, which seems to be a generally satisfactory substrate for Protozoa outside the phytoflagellates, the ability to metabolize a particular monosaccharide may show erratic taxonomic distribution. Galactose, for example, seems to be used readily enough by several strains of *Tetrahymena pyriformis* but not by certain others, and both types of results have been reported from a single laboratory in several cases. In contrast to ciliates, the tested parasitic flagellates (*Crithidia*, *Leishmania*, *Leptomonas*, *Trichomonas*, *Trypanosoma*) all have shown the ability to use galactose.

In the dissimilation of hexoses, a variety of Protozoa follow the Embden-Meyerhof pathway, a series of reactions not dependent upon atmospheric oxygen and leading to the production of pyruvic acid. Protozoa known to use glucose in this way include *Euglena gracilis* var. *bacillaris*, species of *Crithidia*, *Trichomonas* and *Trypanosoma*, malarial parasites, and ciliates (most of the data being based on strains of *Tetrahymena pyriformis*).

The fate of the pyruvic acid which is produced from glucose varies with the species to some extent (Table 5), particularly in such genera as *Trypanosoma*. Certain species (*e.g.*, *T. brucei*, *T. equiperdum*, *T. evansi*, *T. gambiense*, *T. hippicum*, etc.) stop with pyruvic acid. In some of these cases pyruvic acid has been the only product reported; in others, glycerol also has accumulated in appreciable amounts. The presumed origin of

TABLE 5
Products of Monosaccharide Catabolism in a Few Heterotrophs

| Products | T. hippicum | T. cruzi | T. lewisii | C. fasciculata | T. foetus. | T. vaginalis |
|---|---|---|---|---|---|---|
| Acetate | − | + | + | + | + | |
| $CO_2$ | − | + | | + | | |
| Citrate | | + | | | | |
| Ethanol | − | | | + | | |
| Formate | − | | + | + | | |
| Lactate | − | | + | + | | + |
| Malate | − | | | | | + |
| Pyruvate | + | + | + | + | | |
| Succinate | − | + | + | + | + | |

glycerol from dihydroxyacetone phosphate is favored by anaerobic conditions. Other species, such as *T. lewisi*, can produce acetic, lactic and succinic acids; also, in a few cases, formic acid and ethanol have been reported. The insect parasite, *Crithidia oncopelti*, has produced ethanol, glycerol, and succinate, while the related *C. fasciculata* has produced acetate, carbon dioxide, ethanol, formate, lactate, and succinate. Like other trypanosomid flagellates, however, *C. fasciculata* seems unable to carry out complete oxidation of glucose, at least under reported experimental conditions.

Although the operation of an aerobic pathway has been reported in *Crithidia fasciculata* and *Tetrahymena pyriformis*, there is little detailed information about such carbohydrate dissimilation in Protozoa.

In another phase of carbohydrate metabolism, polysaccharides are synthesized by at least many of the Protozoa. The phytoflagellates, with the possible exception of the Chloromonadida, produce polysaccharides for storage as reserves. In certain species, this stored polysaccharide may amount to 15–20 per cent of the dry body weight. In some cases (*Chlamycomonas* spp., certain dinoflagellates) polysaccharides are secreted into the culture medium. Cultures of one of the dinoflagellates, *Katodinium dorsalosulcum*, accumulate in abundance a dense mucoid polysaccharide, apparently a galactan of some sort although containing small amounts of other sugars in addition to galactose (McLaughlin *et al.*, 1960). Such extracellular polysaccharides could be ecologically significant as food for other microorganisms. However, the *Katodinium* polysaccharide has shown antibiotic activity for certain bacteria although it stimulates growth of others.

The storage of polysaccharides is quite common in Protozoa, although the specific type of polysaccharide may vary from group to group. Starches are stored by Phytomonadida, Dinoflagellida and Crypto-monadida, in the last group as fairly uniform refractile bodies readily visible under the microscope. Refractile paramylum bodies, composed also of glucose polymers, are found in Euglenida. A similar material (leucosin) is stored in Chrysomonadida as small to fairly large refractile inclusions. One of the small amoebae, *Acanthamoeba sp.*, synthesizes cellulose but only as a component of the endocyst, the inner layer of the cyst wall. Another superficial deposition of a polysaccharide occurs in *Crithidia fasciculata*, which synthesizes a galactan as a component of its pellicle. Many other Protozoa — Sarcodina, trichomonad flagellates, ciliates — store glycogens as major reserve materials. However, certain parasitic ciliates (*Dasytricha, Entodinium*, etc.) of herbivores store amylo-pectins which differ in chemical structure from the glycogens of various other ciliates. Glycogens from *Tetrahymena pyriformis* and two species of *Trichomonas* have been concentrated and purified for investigation. The molecular structure of the glycogen varies with the species but all three are rather similar to liver glycogen of the rabbit. In certain Protozoa, such as *Stentor* and the cysts of certain parasitic amoebae, the glycogen is stored in fairly large masses; in other cases, glycogen appears as finely granular material either scattered through the cytoplasm or more or less concentrated in one part of the body. The glycogen mass of *Stentor* may be somewhat unusual in that it is partitioned more or less equally between the two daughter organisms in fission.

## Vitamins and Analogous Growth Factors

Protozoa differ considerably in the extent to which they can synthesize the particular vitamins or growth factors they need in metabolism. This means that Protozoa either do or do not require certain vitamins as components of the culture medium. All of the Protozoa which can grow without an external source of vitamins are autotrophs — either photo-autotrophs or heteroautotrophs, depending upon whether they use light or some organic compound as a source of energy. Colorless flagellates capable of synthesizing all their vitamins seem to be very rare, the known examples being *Polytoma obtusum* and *P. uvella*. Other species of *Polytoma* and also the related colorless phyomonads all appear to be *auxotrophs* — that is, they must be supplied with one or more vitamins or growth factors. The chlorophyll-bearing flagellates show a similar diversity in their ability to synthesize vitamins, and some of them need as many vitamins as their close colorless relatives, or occasionally even more than a colorless homologue. The establishment of this generalization was something of a surprise when experimental data forced the discard of the old generalization that any green flagellate is automatically a photoautotroph. It is now apparent that the presence or absence of chlorophyll is not the factor controlling ability to synthesize certain vitamins, although it is clear that many more chlorophyll-bearing than colorless species can carry out these syntheses.

So far as extent of the ability to synthesize vitamins is concerned, available data split Protozoa into two general groups — the phytoflagellates, which can synthesize either all or nearly all of their vitamins, and the typical heterotrophs, which include the Protozoa generally unable to synthesize a number of vitamins. However, the discovery that small amoebae — *Acanthamoeba* sp. (Adam, 1964) and *Hartmanella rhysodes* (Band, 1962) — need only three vitamins, two of which are vitamins needed by many phytoflagellates, raised questions which cannot be answered until more axenic cultures of Sarcodina are available for study. At any rate, the typical heterotrophs are unable to synthesize the majority of the vitamins they need. In contrast, the phytoflagellates which have lost abilities to synthesize vitamins usually need vitamin $B_{12}$ or thiamine or both vitamins, and sometimes biotin in addition to one or both of the others. Any additional requirement seems to be quite rare. The factors responsible for such conformity to a rather set pattern by auxotrophic flagellates remain matters for speculation. If it is assumed that auxotrophic characteristics are the results of biochemical losses sustained in evolution of these flagellates, there remains the problem of explaining why such losses in biosynthetic capacity should involve these three vitamins in particular and on such a wide taxonomic scale.

The rest of the Protozoa — excepting *Acanthamoeba, Hartmanella* and any other Protozoa with similar abilities — apparently rival the higher animals in the complexity of their requirements, except that they do not seem to need ascorbic acid or such fat – soluble vitamins as A and D. Although this nutritional cleavage of the phylum obviously parallels to some extent the taxonomic arrangement of phytoflagellates on the one hand and animal-like Protozoa on the other, the small taxonomic groups seem so far to show no specific nutritional patterns which might distinguish one group from another.

The bearing of such data on phylogenetic questions is uncertain. If one accepts the common assumption that the phytoflagellates are more primitive than other Protozoa, it would seem necessary to endorse the postulate that organisms such as the Phytomonadida, with enzyme systems for synthesizing all or most of their vitamins, are more primitive than Protozoa which lack such systems. This, of course, would imply that evolution of the specialized animal-like Protozoa has involved the loss of such mechanisms for biosynthesis developed earlier by their supposedly more primitive ancestors.

The determination of vitamin requirements is one of the more exacting phases of experimental work in the investigation of protozoan nutrition. The procedures obviously demand axenic cultures in chemically defined media. Beyond these elementary precautions, it is essential to avoid chemical contamination of glassware and culture media, since certain growth factors are active in surprisingly low concentrations. For example some of the dinoflagellates are sensitive to vitamin $B_{12}$ at a concentration of 0.03 m$\mu$g/100 ml (Provasoli, 1958a). Such sensitivity intensifies the problems of avoiding contamination with certain growth factors and consequently increases the difficulty of preparing control media free from such growth factors. Investigations in this field may be facilitated to some extent by subjecting organisms to metabolic stresses induced by maintenance at unusually high temperatures. Thus, raising the temperature of incubation from 34 to 38° C. increased the $B_{12}$ requirement of *Ochromonas malahmensis* about 3000 times, in addition to increasing the demands for certain other growth factors and metabolites (Hutner *et al.*, 1957).

### SPECIFIC VITAMIN REQUIREMENTS

Thiamine is probably the vitamin most likely to be needed by a protozoon. This vitamin, used in the production of cocarboxylase, is metabolically important in microorganisms generally as well as in other types of cells. For undetermined reasons, the ability to synthesize thiamine is a property which can be lost rather easily. Even many of the green flagellates lack the ability to synthesize this vitamin, although some of the losers have close relatives which can do the job. This thiamine requirement of phytoflagellates shows no correlation with the presence or absence of chlorophyll (Provasoli, 1958) or with taxonomic relationships. In the Cryptomonadida, for example, *Cryptomonas ovata* and *Cyanophora paradoxa* need no thiamine while *Hemiselmis virescens* and *Rhodomonas lens* require the vitamin. All four species contain chlorophyll. Similar differences have been observed within the genus *Hymenomonas* (chrysomonad flagellates). Among the colorless Phytomonadida a similar situation is found. Thiamine or one of its moieties is needed by *Polytoma caudatum* and *P. ocellatum*, whereas *P. obtusum* and *P. uvella* have no thiamine requirement. Comparable contrasts have turned up in the dinoflagellates: *Gymnodinium breve* needs thiamine but *G. splendens* and several other dinoflagellates do not. Likewise, the chrysomonad, *Hymenomonas elongata*, needs thiamine but *H. carterae* does not. The work of Lwoff and his colleagues showed that these losses of synthesizing ability may occur in stages in colorless Phytomonadida. Thus, *Polytoma obtusum* and *P. uvella* can synthesize the complete thiamine molecule. The closely related *P. caudatum* and *P. ocellatum* must be supplied with the thiazole moiety of thiamine, although both species can synthesize the pyrimidine component and combine the two in production of thiamine. Technically, the latter two have a thiazole requirement but not a true thiamine requirement. More recent findings indicate a similar status for the colorless dinoflagellate, *Oxyrrhis marina*. *Polytomella caeca* and also a colorless cryptomonad flagellate, *Chilomonas paramecium*, need both the thiazole and pyrimidine moieties; given these, the flagellates can synthesize their own thiamine. One unexpected observation on *P. caeca* is that an increased thiamine supplement protects the flagellates against too much alcohol because the extra vitamin permits growth on concentrations which would otherwise be inhibitory. *P. caeca* can grow in 1.0 per cent ethanol provided the thiamine supplement is increased to 12.0 mg/100 ml, or in 1.4 per cent propanol with thiamine at 32 mg/100 ml (Wise *et al.*, 1961).

The last step in this biochemical regression is seen in such typical heterotrophs as *Tetrahymena pyriformis*. Several strains of this species, tested in different laboratories, have shown no ability to use the pyrimidine and thiazole moieties as a substitute for thiamine. In addition to eliciting a marked growth-response in a suitable thiamine-deficient medium, a generous supplement of thiamine has tripled the longevity of *T. pyriformis* in a medium with low thiamine content. Hence, this ciliate has a genuine requirement for thiamine. The same situation apparently exists in the chrysomonad flagellate, *Ochromonas malhamensis*, although some of its relatives (species of *Synura*) evidently can synthesize thiamine from simple precursors (Provasoli, 1958).

The rigidity of the thiamine requirement has interested some protozoologists. In Lwoff's laboratory, it was found that several different analogues were fair to good substitutes for the natural thiazole and pyrimidine components of thiamine in colorless phytoflagellates. The case of *Tetrahymena pyriformis* has been a less placid one. At one time or another, reports from different laboratories suggested that at least certain strains of this species can synthesize thiamine. In one case, the investigators reversed their early conclusion after it became possible to replace products of natural origin with chemically known substitutes. In another case, it is possible that the results of a bacteriological assay of *Tetrahymena* cultures, negative just after inoculation, became positive after incubation because the ciliates had digested a natural supplement (yeast nucleic acid). Another possibility is that differences in enzyme/ substrate ratios reported for the preliminary digestion in the initial and and final assays might have had a significant influence on the amount of thiamine released for "detection" by the assay organisms. In any case, more proof is needed before *T. pyriformis* as a species can be credited with the ability to synthesize thiamine.

At present, it appears that among the phytoflagellates a thiamine requirement is rare in green species of Phytomonadida (some of which are truly photoautotrophic), the usual thing in green and colorless Euglenida, and common in Cryptomonadida and Chrysomonadida. One of the Chrysomonadida, *Ochromonas malhamensis*, has been used successfully for assaying thiamine in blood and other body fluids. A thiamine requirement is rather uncommon in chlorophyll-bearing Dinoflagellida. Except for *Oxyrrhis marina*, which can substitute thiazole for thiamine, the specific requirements of colorless dinoflagellates have not been reported. Among the Zoomastigophora, a thiamine requirement has been determined for several parasitic species (*Crithidia fasciculata*, *C. oncopelti*, *Leishmania tarentolae*). Sarcodina needing thiamine are represented by

*Acanthamoeba, Hartmanella* and *Labyrinthula*. All the ciliates which have been tested adequately require thiamine and, except for *Tetrahymena pyriformis*, no ciliate has been accused of synthesizing the vitamin.

Vitamin $B_{12}$ is required by phytoflagellates at least as commonly as thiamine, or even more commonly in at least one group. The majority of dinoflagellates tested so far actually do not need thiamine, but nearly all of them require vitamin $B_{12}$ (Provasoli, 1958; Provasoli and McLaughlin, 1963). Much as in the case of thiamine, a requirement for $B_{12}$ may be present or absent in closely related species — *e.g.*, different species of the chrysomonad genus, *Hymenmonas*. Nearly all protozoan species now known to require vitamin $B_{12}$ are phytoflagellates. The exceptions are small amoebae — *Acanthamoeba* sp. (Adam, 1959) and *Hartmanella rhysodes* (Band, 1962). Both of these, like many phytoflagellates, need thiamine as well as $B_{12}$, and both *Acanthamoeba* and *H. rhysodes* need biotin in addition. Such a pattern of vitamin requirements is not representative of the heterotrophic Protozoa but it would fit snugly among the lists of requirements reported for phytoflagellates.

Specificity of the $B_{12}$ requirement varies in the sense that species differ in their ability to use particular analogues as substitutes for cyanocobalamin (vitamin $B_{12}$). *Ochromonas malhamensis*, several marine chrysomonad flagellates (species of *Isochrysis, Microglena, Prymnesium* and *Syracosphaera*), a cryptomonad (*Hemiselmis virescens*) and a few species of *Gymnodiuium* (all marine) show sensitivity to vitamin $B_{12}$, its synthetic benzimidazole and dichlorobenzimidazole analogues and factor I. The dichlorobenzimidazole analogue seems to be about as active as natural $B_{12}$ for these flagellates (Provasoli, 1958a). Such responses are comparable to those of mammals. *Euglena gracilis* (used in the *Euglena* assay for $B_{12}$), one of the chrysomonads (Monochrysis lutheri) and certain dinoflagellates (*Amphidinium* spp.) respond to such other analogues as pseudovitamin $B_{12}$, factor A and factor H. However, the activity of the last two analogues for *Amphidinium* sp. is much lower than that of vitamin $B_{12}$.

The protozoological assay of vitamin $B_{12}$ has been carried out so far with *Ochromonas malhamensis* and *Euglena gracilis* (especially strain z), the former having achieved an "official" British status. Both organisms show certain desirable features. *E. gracilis*, which responds to 0.25 $\mu\mu g/ml$, is more sensitive than *O. malhamensis* but is less restricted in its response to analogues of $B_{12}$. The narrower specificity of *O. malhamensis* is a practical compensation for somewhat lower sensitivity, and this species is being used extensively for bioassay of clinical materials. In view of the use of *O. malhamensis* in such assays, it is interesting that *O. danica* can grow without $B_{12}$, although it does require biotin and thiamine (Aaronson and Baker, 1959). Results obtained with *E. gracilis* represent an estimate of "total $B_{12}$ activity" of a sample, while the responses of *O. malhamensis* supply a more accurate estimate of the $B_{12}$ significant in mammalian metabolism.

Vitamin $B_{12}$ is of ecological interest because it is required by some of the flagellates and diatoms making up the so-called meadows of the ocean and also by phytoflagellates commonly responsible for "red tides." As a result, the $B_{12}$ concentration of seawater is a factor of some importance in the marine food chain. Also, through its apparent influence on the phenomenon of red tide, $B_{12}$ is indirectly involved in the death of marine fish during such overgrowths of dinoflagellates and, less commonly, in the "mussel poisoning" of man following consumption of mussels which have eaten dinoflagellates and concentrated the potent toxin in their tissues. The common assumption that fluctuations in the $B_{12}$ content of seawater are involved in red tides raises questions about the origin of the $B_{12}$ which increases the vitamin content to a level at which blooms become possible. Two potential sources are apparent: organisms belonging to the normal flora of seawater; and washings from the land draining into coastal waters. The common sequence of a period of heavy rains and then an excessive growth of dinoflagellates has suggested that, among the various effects produced by extensive drainage from the land, an influx of nutrients could be responsible for these blooms of microorganisms. Recent tests of *Gymnodinium breve*, one of the common red-tide flagellates, indicate that excessive populations of these organisms are not really the result of extra food because *G. breve* closely approaches being a strict photoautotroph (Aldrich, 1962). This leaves an increase in concentration of growth factors, such as vitamin $B_{12}$, as a possible explanation which does not conflict with available information. As for the origin of the $B_{12}$ in observed fluctuations in concentration, some of it obviously could have been produced on land and merely washed into the ocean. However, many of the marine bacteria and at least a few of the blue-green algae are known producers of $B_{12}$, and an increase in production obviously could result from land drainage which would supply more food for growth of $B_{12}$-synthesizers. Another source could be the death and decomposition of planktonic organisms and littoral seaweed containing the vitamin, since the accumulation of $B_{12}$ by certain seaweeds has been reported. In addition to the release of $B_{12}$ from decaying organisms, another result would be the contribution of extra food for $B_{12}$-synthesizing bacteria of the immediate region, with a subsequent increase in concentration of the vitamin in the seawater. So far, only a beginning has been made in tracing fluctuations in the $B_{12}$ content of coastal waters and the open ocean. Much more information is needed before the ecological significance of this vitamin can be evaluated accurately. The accumulation of such data obviously depends upon the perfection of assay techniques suitable for seawater of different salinities.

Biotin is the third of the vitamins which are required more or less commonly by phytoflagellates. However, this one apparently is synthesized by more species than the other two. Thus, Phytomonadida seem to need biotin very rarely if at all. Euglenida and Cryptomonadida resemble the phytomonads in this respect. A few of the marine dinoflagellates and chrysomonads, on the other hand, show a definite biotin requirement, most of the findings being reported from Provasoli's laboratory (Provasoli, 1958a). Certain freshwater phytoflagellates, such as *Ochromonas* spp., also need biotin (Table 6), and this requirement also has been reported for such parasitic flagellates as *Crithidia fasciculata* and *Leishmania tarentolae*. As noted in the table, the list now includes certain small amoebae as well as various ciliates, some of which are specified in the table.

*Pantothenic acid* (Table 6, PA) is required by several flagellates, none of which is a phytoflagellate, and by all the ciliates which have been tested adequately. One ciliate, *Tetrahymena pyriformis*, has been used for bioassay of clinical materials. There are also data strongly suggesting a pantothenate requirement for trichomonad flagellates and malarial parasites, although one of the latter (*Plasmodium lophurae*) needs coenzyme A itself rather than a pantothenate precursor.

Pyridoxine (Table 6, $B_6$), or else pyridoxamine or pyridoxal, is a known requirement of two flagellates and certain ciliates (*Glaucoma chattoni*, four species of *Tetrahymena*); such a requirement probably is a characteristic of *Paramecium* spp. also. The existence of mating type strains of *T. pyriformis* with and without a pyridoxine requirement made possible the determination that this requirement is a dominant trait

TABLE 6
Vitamin Requirements of a Few Heterotrophs

| Species | $B_1$ | $B_2$ | $B_6$ | Biotin | PGA | NA | TA | PA | Lipids |
|---|---|---|---|---|---|---|---|---|---|
| Trypanosomidae: | | | | | | | | | |
| Crithidia fasciculata | + | + | +[2] | + | + | + | | + | |
| Leishmania tarentolae | + | + | +[1] | | | + | | + | |
| Sarcodina: | | | | | | | | | |
| Acanthamoeba sp.* | + | − | − | + | − | − | − | − | − |
| Hartmanella rhysodes* | + | − | − | + | − | − | − | − | − |
| Ciliata: | | | | | | | | | |
| Glaucoma chattoni | + | + | + | + | + | + | + | + | ± |
| Paramecium multimicro-nucleatum | + | + | + | ± | + | + | ± | + | + |
| Tetrahymena pyriformis | + | + | + | + | + | + | + | + | − |
| T. setifera | + | + | + | + | + | + | + | + | + |

(+) Required;  (±) probable requirement;  (−) not required.
[1]pyridoxal or pyridoxamine, replaceable by pyridoxine;  + choline;  [2]pyridoxamine instead of pyridoxine.
*These species need vitamin $B_{12}$ also.

which is inherited in Mendelian fashion in *T. pyriformis* (Elliott and Clark, 1958). The ability to synthesize pyridoxine is relatively rare in this species: only 41 such strains were found in a total of 2500 tested clones. This seems to be the only case in which inheritance of the capacity to synthesize a vitamin has been traced in ciliates. The pyridoxal requirement of *Leishmania tarentolae* can be satisfied with a combination of choline and pyridoxine (Trager, 1957a).

Riboflavin (Table 6, $B_2$) is needed by one of the phytoflagellates (the phagotrophic *Peranema trichophorum*), at least two trypanosomid flagellates, and all the ciliates which have been tested carefully. Data which are not entirely conclusive indicate that trichomonad flagellates have the same requirement. Recent observations on *Leishmania tarentolae* relate the presence of a long and effective flagellum to a fairly high concentration of riboflavin in the culture medium. With decreasing concentrations of the vitamin, the average length of the flagellum and the percentage of flagellated specimens both decreased. At a minimal concentration which still permitted moderate growth in serial transfers, all the organisms lacked flagella (Trager and Rudzinska, 1964). Whether such a vitamin deficiency could be involved in the metamorphosis accompanying the shift to a vertebrate host is a matter for speculation.

A requirement for nicotinic acid (Table 6, NA) shows a distribution similar to that of riboflavin requirements. Old reports of biosynthesis by *Tetrahymena pyriformis* have been negated by establishment of strains in chemically defined media or are not generally accepted on technical grounds.

Thioctic acid, or α-lipoic acid, first recognized as a requirement of *Tetrahymena pyriformis* among the Protozoa, is now known to be needed by three other species of *Tetrahymena* and also *Glaucoma chattoni*, probably also by *Paramecium* spp. and various other ciliates not yet tested adequately. The status of this growth factor as a requirement for other groups of Protozoa is still uncertain, although it seems clear that some of the carefully investigated species do not have a requirement for thioctic acid.

A member of the folic acid group (folic acid, its diglutamate and hexaglutamate, and folinic acid) is needed by all of the ciliates which have been tested carefully (Table 6, PGA). Among the trypanosomid flagellates, *Crithidia fasciculata* needs folic acid while *C. oncopelti* can get along on *p*-aminobenzoic acid as a substitute (Newton, 1957). This intrageneric difference may be related to the presence of a bacterial infection, presumably with a symbiotic organism, in *C. oncopelti* (Gill and Vogel, 1963). Indirect evidence obtained by reversal of antimetabolite inhibition suggests that malarial parasites have a definite need for folic acid. Early reports that folic acid needed by *T. pyriformis* could be replaced by one of its analogues (aminopterin) were contradicted by the discovery that the samples of aminopterin used were contaminated with enough folic acid to account for the observed effects on growth.

Biopterin, or the *"Crithidia* factor," is an unconjugated pteridine needed by *Crithidia fasciculata*. A few related pteridines are fair to good substitutes for biopterin. This requirement of *C. fasciculata* has been applied to a bioassay technique for pteridines (Nathan *et al.*, 1958).

Hematin is a requirement of certain trypanosomid flagellates but not all of them, the requirement presumably reflecting an inability to synthesize protoporphyrins. Trypanosomes need the growth-factor. Some of the related species which do not have such a requirement are parasites of invertebrates rather than vertebrates. This ecological difference is not the primary factor determining the existence or lack of a hematin requirement, as indicated by the need for hematin in a parasite of mosquitoes, *Crithidia fasciculata*.

Lipid requirements, reviewed recently by Hutner and Holz (1962), have been reported for some of the Protozoa. These particular species are unable to synthesize a specific long-chain fatty acid in some cases; in others, the disability may involve a sterol or, in at least certain species, both a sterol and a fatty acid (as in *Trichomonas* spp. and *Paramecium* spp., for example). Although most of the recognized lipid requirements have been reported for Protozoa which can grow only in very complex culture media — *e.g.*, trichomonad flagellates, certain ciliates — such a requirement also has turned up in less exacting species. Isolated examples are known in Euglenida (*Peranema trichophorum*) and Dinoflagellida (*Oxyrrhis marina*), orders which contain mostly flagellates with rather simple food requirements. Both of these exceptional phytoflagellates are phagotrophs and the habit of eating other microorganisms may have facilitated such a loss of biosynthetic capacity. The ciliates with recognized lipid requirements also are phagotrophs but the method of feeding apparently is not a major factor in this group. *Tetrahymena pyriformis*, for example, is an enthusiastic phagotroph but does not, except at unusually high temperatures, need a lipid in its diet; three other species of *Tetrahymena* do have a sterol requirement at normal incubation temperatures. Since endoparasitism might favor biosynthetic losses, it is no surprise to find lipid requirements in trichomonad flagellates and at least some of the trypanosomes.

If lipids are metabolically important in Protozoa generally, it would be suspected that species without a lipid requirement can synthesize all these substances they need. Some of the scanty evidence available at present supports such an assumption. Sterols have been recovered from certain phytoflagellates — *Euglena gracilis*, *Ochromonas danica*, *O. malhamensis* — and from one of the cellular slime molds (*Dictyostelium discoideum*) maintained in culture media to which such growth factors had not been added. On the other hand, strains of *Tetrahymena pyriformis* (which do not require sterols) do not accumulate significant quantities of such substances (Aaronson and Baker, 1961). In contrast to such flagellates as *Ochromonas*, tests for ability to synthesize cholesterol have been negative in *Trichomonas foetus*.

When a lipid requirement does exist, a few lipids are typically much more active than others for a particular species, and some are apparently useless. Such differences in activity may not depend entirely upon chemical structure as such since the rate of uptake also could influence the results when activity is measured in terms of influence on population growth. Fatty acid requirements include stearic acid for *Trypanosoma cruzi*, oleic or stearic acid for *Paramecium multimicronucleatum*, linoleic and oleic acids for *P. caudatum*, $C_{14}$-$C_{18}$ saturated and $C_{18}$-$C_{22}$ unsaturated fatty acids for trichomonads (species of *Hypotrichomonas, Monocercomonas, Trichomonas, Tritrichomonas*). Among the biologically active sterols, stigmasterol is one of the most effective for *Paramecium* spp. but is unsatisfactory for *Trichomonas gallinae*. Cholesterol is particularly satisfactory for three species of *Tetrahymena* and satisfies the sterol requirement of various trichomonads but seems useless to *Paramecium aurelia*. The same is true for ergosterol. The unusual euglenoid, *Peranema trichophorum*, favors cholesterol, and the same sterol is one of the most active ones for *Labyrinthula* spp., the unusual monorail sarcodinids.

Although sterols are definitely needed by certain Protozoa and are known to be synthesized by at least a few other species which show no sterol requirement, the significance of these substances in protozoan metabolism in general has not been determined. It is interesting, however, that a sterol extracted from a cellular slime mold has shown activity similar to that of *acrasin*, the substance stimulating aggregation of amoeboid stages into the pseudoplasmodium stage in the life cycle of these organisms.

Certain miscellaneous factors active in particular Protozoa have not yet been characterized accurately in some cases. Among these substances is a so-called "protein factor" needed by *Paramecium caudatum* in microgram quantities for growth in an otherwise defined medium. Activity of the factor is destroyed by chemical or enzymatic hydrolysis. The complexity of the "factor" is suggested by the identification of sixteen amino acids in hydrolysates. Somewhat surprisingly, this requirement has recently been met by addition of a synthetic magnesium silicate to the medium.

Another member of the miscellaneous group is, at the same time, an apparently unusual requirement for Protozoa. An alcohol, either ethanol or methanol, is needed by *Tetrahymena setifera* in quantities which almost qualify such a beverage as a growth factor. Whether this relationship of alcohol to growth of *T. setifera* depends upon solvent properties or other attributes has not been reported. Another unusual requirement of ciliates is that for choline, recently reported by Elliott's laboratory for several European strains of *T. pyriformis*.

Another unusual type of growth factor is chloramphenicol, an antibiotic which stimulates growth of the chrysomonad *Poteriochromonas stipitata* (Isenberg *et al.*, 1963), but interferes with synthesis of proteins in such susceptible microorganisms as *Escherichia coli*.

Certain other "factors" apparently are significant in stimulating morphological changes (and perhaps physiological ones also) in the life cycles of certain parasites. Unidentified substances, present in washed red corpuscles, were essential for regression of the trypanosomal to the crithidial stage of *Trypanosoma conorhini* in laboratory cultures incubated at 25–28° C. (Deane and Kirchner, 1963). The effect of this "metamorphosis factor" was prevented by incubating the organisms at 37° C. In the analogous case of *Trypanosoma vivax*, transformation of "insect" stages into infective stages (capable of infecting a vertebrate host) has been induced *in vitro* by maintaining the flagellates at 38° C. in tsetse fly tissue culture (Trager, 1959).

Experiments with flagellates of the wood roach (Cleveland, Burke, and Karlson, 1960) illustrate an analogous effect of ecdysone, the molting hormone produced by the host, on the life cycle of intestinal parasites. The injection of exogenous ecdysone into an intermolt nymph or adult roach (neither of which contains ecdysone of its own) induces gametogenesis in the flagellates. Such changes in the flagellates also are accelerated (and so is molting of the host) when ecdysone is injected into a nymph during the molting period. Excessive amounts of ecdysone, however, may overstimulate the flagellates and lead to degeneration and death. Since ecdysone stimulates reproduction of the flagellates it may, in this sense, qualify as a "growth factor." In addition, however, the molting hormone also induces differentiation of the flagellates into gametes.

In a somewhat similar case, excystment of *Gymnodinioides* sp. and *G. inkystans* occurs under natural conditions shortly before the actual molting of their crustacean hosts. In the laboratory, excystment occurs if the cysts are taken from the gills of a crab near the molting period. Also, blood from such a crab is a more effective stimulus than that from a crab which is not just about to molt (Trager, 1957).

A similar example involves effects of a vertebrate hormone on a parasite of vertebrates. Encystment of *Opalina ranarum* apparently can be induced by injecting testosterone into parasitized *Rana temporaria* (El-Mofty and Smyth, 1960).

A switch on the situation described for the wood-roach and its flagellates involves *Nosema* sp., a cnidosporidian parasite which synthesizes a substance with high juvenile hormone activity for the nymphal stage of roaches (Fisher, 1963).

## EFFECTS OF STRESS ON FOOD REQUIREMENTS

It has been known for many years that increases in temperature modify the nutritional requirements of various bacteria, sometimes by increasing the need for particular nutrients, in other cases by precipitating a new need for some metabolite as a critical temperature is reached. More recent investigations on certain Protozoa have shown that increases in temperature of incubation induce similar changes in growth requirements of these organisms (Hutner, *et al.*, 1957; Hutner, *et al.*, 1958).

Such effects were shown strikingly in *Ochromonas malhamensis* (Hutner, *et al.*, 1957). In the shift from 34 to 38°C. the requirement for thiamine was increased about 1000 times. Increase in the $B_{12}$ requirement was of at least the same order. The needs for certain metals — iron, magnesium, manganese, zinc — also rose sharply with increasing temperature; a similar rise in the need for copper was reported later (Hutner, *et al.*, 1958). Several apparently specific amino acid requirements also developed at the higher temperatures, and extra purines and pyrimidines became stimulatory. Requirements for growth of *Crithidia fasciculata* also were influenced by increasing temperature (Hutner *et al.*, 1958): a mixture of trace metals (calcium, copper, iron, magnesium), interchangeable with an organic mixture (glutamate, lactate, succinate), became necessary in shifting from 24 to 32°C. At temperatures above 32.3°C. both the metals and the organic supplement were required.

Such changes in dietary requirements may reflect changes in rates of enzyme activities. In the usual biothermal range, a species may meet its metabolic demands from an available supply of foods, metals and vitamins. At higher temperatures, aside from any potential damage to specific enzymes, metabolic rates increase, resulting in increased needs for various nutrients. Effects are apt to be noticed first in materials present only in traces. Thus, metals or vitamins may rapidly become scarce, so as to retard or prevent growth. Likewise, scarcity of even a non-essential metabolite may intensify the need for a metal or vitamin involved in production of the substance under normal conditions. Or, if some component of the medium has been enabling the organism to bypass a potential need for a certain growth factor, increasing needs under thermal stress may induce an apparently new need for a growth factor, rather than just an increased demand for a specific factor.

## Bibliography

AARONSON, S., and H. BAKER, 1959. A comparative biochemical study of two species of *Ochromonas*. *J. Protozool.* **6**, 282–284.

AARONSON, S., and H. NATHAN, 1954. Utilization of imidazole counterparts of purines in microbial systems. *Biochim. Biophys. Acta* **15**, 306–307.

ADAM, K. M. G., 1959. The growth of *Acanthamoeba* sp. in a chemically defined medium. *J. Gen. Microbiol.* **21**, 519–529.

———— 1964. The amino acid requirements of *Acanthamoeba* sp. Neff. *J. Protozool.* **10**, 98–100.

ALDRICH, D. V., 1962. Photoautotrophy in *Gymnodinium breve*. *Science* **137**, 988–990.

APP, A. A. and A. T. JAGENDORF, 1963. Repression of chloroplast development in *Euglena gracilis* by substrate. *J. Protozool.* **10**, 340–343.

BALAMUTH, W., 1962. Effects of some environmental factors upon growth and encystation of *Entamoeba invadens*. *J. Parasitol.* **48**, 101–109.

BAND, N. R., 1962. The amino acid requirements of the soil amoeba, *Hartmanella rhysodes*. *J. Protozool.* **9**, 377–379.

———— 1963. Extrinsic factors for encystation by the soil amoeba, *Hartmanella rhysodes*. *J. Protozool.* **10**, 101–106.

BÉ, A. W. H. and B. D. ERICSON, 1963. Aspects of calcification in planktonic Foraminifera (Sarcodina). *Ann. N. Y. Acad. Sci.* **100**, 65–81.

BIRDSEY, E. C. and V. H. LYNCH, 1962. Utilization of nitrogen compounds by unicellular algae. *Science* **137**, 763–764.

BOVEE, E. C., 1960. Studies concerning the effects of nutrition on morphology of amebas. I. *Mayorella cultura* Bovee, on abundant and starvation quantities. *Amer. Midl. Nat.* **63**, 257–269.

BROWN, H. P. and M. M. JENKINS, 1962. A protozoon (*Dileptus:* Ciliata) predatory upon Metazoa. *Science* **136**, 710.

BURBANCK, W. D., 1942. Physiology of the ciliate *Colpidium colpoda*. I. The effect of various bacteria as food on the division rate of *Colpidium colpoda*. *Physiol. Zool.* **15**, 342–362.

———— and J. D. EISEN, 1960. The inadequacy of monobacterially fed *Paramecium aurelia* as food for *Didinium nasutum*. *J. Protozool.* **7**, 201-206.

CHADWICK, A., 1961. The fate of radioactively labelled glycine introduced into *Amoeba proteus* and *Stentor coeruleus*. *Exper. Cell Res.* **25**, 131–148.

CHANG, S. L., 1958. Cultural, cytological and ecological observations on the amoeba stage of *Naegleria gruberi*. *J. Gen. Microbiol*. **18**, 565–578.

CHAPMAN-ANDRESEN, C. and H. HOLTER, 1955. Studies on the ingestion of $C^{14}$ glucose by pinocytosis in the amoeba. *Exper. Cell. Res. Suppl*. **3**, 52–63.

CIRILLO, V. C., 1962. Mechanism of arabinose transport in *Tetrahymena pyriformis*. *J. Bact*. **84**, 754–758.

CLAFF, C. L., V. C. DEWEY, and G. W. KIDDER, 1941. Feeding mechanisms and nutrition in three species of *Bresslaua*. *Biol. Bull*. **81**, 221–234.

CLEVELAND, L. R., A. W. BURKE, JR., and P. KARLSON, 1960. Ecdysone induced modifications in the sexual cycles of the protozoa of *Cryptocercus*. *J. Protozool*. **7**, 229–239.

COELHO, J., and D. V. REYE, 1963. On hemoglobin inhibition of the growth of *Euglena gracilis*. *J. Protozool*. **10**, 473–477.

COOK, J. R., 1963. Adaptations in growth and division in *Euglena* effected by the energy supply. *J. Protozool*. **10**, 436–444.

COSGROVE, W. B., 1950. Studies on the question of chemoautotrophy in *Chilomonas paramecium*. *Physiol. Zool*. **23**, 73–84.

COWPERTHWAITE, J., M. M. WEBER, L. PACKER and S. H. HUTNER, 1953. Nutrition of *Herpetomonas (Strigomonas) culicidarum* Ann. N. Y. Acad. Sci. **56**, 972–981.

DANFORTH, W., 1953. Oxidative metabolism of *Euglena*. *Arch. Biochem. Biophys*. **46**, 164–173.

———— 1961. Oxidative assimilation of acetate by *Euglena*. Carbon balance and effects of ethanol. *J. Protozool*. **8**, 152–158.

DEANE, M., and E. KIRCHNER, 1963. Life cycle of *Trypanosoma conorhini*. Influence of temperature and other factors on growth and morphogenesis. *J. Protozool*. **10**, 391–400.

DEWEY, V. C., and G. W. KIDDER, 1958. Amino acid antagonisms in *Tetrahymena*. *Arch. Biochem. Biophys*. **73**, 29–37.

DORAN, D. J., 1957. Studies on trichomonads. I. The metabolism of *Tritrichomonas foetus* and trichomonads from the nasal cavity and cecum of swine. *J. Protozool*. **4**, 182–190.

ELLIOTT, A. M., and G. M. CLARK, 1958. Genetic studies of the pyridoxine mutant in variety two of *Tetrahymena pyriformis*. *J. Protozool*. **5**, 235–240.

———— 1958a. Genetic studies of the serine mutant in variety nine of *Tetrahymena pyriformis*. *J. Protozool*. **5**, 240–246.

EL-MOFTY, M., and J. D. SMYTH, 1960. Endocrine control of sexual reproduction in *Opalina ranarum* in *Rana temporaria*. *Nature* **186**, 559.

FISHER, F. M., JR., 1963. Production of host endocrine substances by parasites. *Ann. N. Y. Acad. Sci*. **113**, 63–73.

GILL, J. W., and H. J. VOGEL, 1962. Lysine synthesis and phylogeny: biochemical evidence for a bacterial-type endosymbiote in the protozoon *Herpetomonas (Strigomonas) oncopelti*. *Biochim. Biophys. Acta* **56**, 200–220.

GROSS, J. A., and T. L. JAHN, 1962. Cellular responses to thermal and photo stress. I. *Euglena* and *Chlamydomonas*. *J. Protozool*. **9**, 340–346.

HALL, R. P., 1954. Effects of certain metal ions on growth of *Tetrahymena pyriformis*. *J. Protozool*. **1**, 74–79.

———— 1954a. Data on the metal requirements of *Tetrahymena pyriformis*. *Trans. N. Y. Acad. Sci.* **16**, 418–419.

HAMILTON, L., 1953. Utilization of purines for nucleic acid synthesis in chrysomonads and other organisms. *Ann. N. Y. Acad. Sci.* **56**, 961–968.

HARMAN, W. J., and J. O. CORLISS, 1956. Isolation of earthworm setae by the use of histophagous Protozoa. *Trans. Amer. Micr. Soc.* **75**, 332–333.

HOLZ, G. G., JR., 1954. The oxidative metabolism of a cryptomonad flagellate, *Chilomonas paramecium*. *J. Protozool*. **1**, 114–120.

————, J. ERWIN, B. WAGNER, and N. ROSENBAUM, 1962. The nutrition of *Tetrahymena setifera* HZ-1: sterol and alcohol requirements. *J. Protozool*. **9**, 359–363.

HOLZ, G. G., JR., B. WAGNER, J. ERWIN and D. KESSLER, 1961. The nutrition of *Glaucoma chattoni* A. *J. Protozool*. **8**, 192–199.

HUTNER, S. H., S. AARONSON, H. A. NATHAN, S. SCHER and A. CURY, 1958. Trace elements in microorganisms: the temperature approach, in Lamb, C. A., O. G. Bentley and J. M. Beattie, *Trace Elements*, New York: Academic Press 1958, pp. 47–65.

————, H. BAKER, S. AARONSON, H. A. NATHAN, E. RODRIGUEZ, S. LOCKWOOD, M. SANDERS and R. A. PETERSEN, 1957. Growing *Ochromonas malhamensis* above 35°C. *J. Protozool*. **4**, 259–269.

HUTNER, S. H., A. CURY and H. BAKER, 1958. Microbiological assays. *Anal. Chem.* **30**, 849–886.

HUTNER, S. H., and G. G. HOLZ, JR., 1962. Lipid requirements of microorganisms. *Ann. Rev. Microbiol*. **16**, 189–204.

HUTNER, S. H., and L. Provasoli 1955. Comparative biochemistry of flagellates, in HUTNER, S. H., and A. LWOFF, *Biochemistry and Physiology of Protozoa*, New York: Academic Press, 1955, 17–43.

HUTNER, S. H., L. PROVASOLI, A. SCHATZ, and C. P. HASKINS, 1950. Some approaches to the study of the role of metals in the metabolism of microorganisms. *Proc. Amer. Philos. Soc.* **94**, 152–170.

ISENBERG, H. D., J. I. BERKMAN and V. TAVKAR, 1963. Chloramphenicol-induced increase and tetracycline-mediated inhibition of cell yields of *Poteriochromonas stipitata;* ineffectiveness of other antibiotics. *J. Protozool*. **10**, 411–412.

ISENBERG, H. D., L. S. LAVINE, M. L. MOSS, D. KUPFERSTEIN and P. E. LEAR, 1963. Calcification in a marine coccolithophorid. *Ann. N. Y. Acad. Sci.* **109**, 49–64.

ISENBERG, H. D., L. S. LAVINE and H. WEISSFELLNER, 1963. The suppression of mineralization in a coccolithophorid by an inhibitor of carbonic anhydrase. *J. Protozool*. **10**, 477–479.

JANOVY, T., JR., 1963. Monsterism in *Dileptus* (Ciliata) fed on planarians (*Dugesia tigrina*). *J. Protozool*. **10**, 428–430.

JOHNSON, D. F., 1936. Growth of *Glaucoma ficaria* Kahl in cultures with single species of other microorganisms. *Arch. f. Protistenk.* **86**, 359–378.

JOHNSON, W. H., 1936. Studies on the nutrition and reproduction of *Paramecium*. *Physiol. Zool.* **9**, 1–14.

———— 1956. Nutrition of Protozoa. *Ann. Rev. Microbiol.* **10**, 193–212.

———— and C. A. MILLER, 1957. The nitrogen requirements of *Paramecium multimicronucleatum. Physiol. Zool.*, **30**, 106–113.

KIDDER, G. W., V. C. DEWEY, and R. C. FULLER, 1954. Nitrogen requirements of *Glaucoma scintillans* and *Colpidium campylum. Proc. Soc. Exp. Biol. Med.* **86**, 685–689.

KIDDER, G. W., and B. N. DUTTA, 1958. The growth and nutrition of *Crithidia fasciculata. J. Gen. Microbiol.* **18**, 621–638.

KLEIN, R. L., 1961. Homeostatic mechanisms for cation regulation in *Acanthamoeba* sp. *Exper. Cell Res.* **25**, 571–584.

LEE, J. J., H. D. FREUDENTHAL, W. A. MULLER, V. KOSSOV, S. PIERCE and R. GROSSMAN, 1963. Growth and physiology of foraminifers in the laboratory: Part 3. Initial studies of *Rosalina floridana* (Cushman). *Micropaleontology* **9**, 449–466.

LEE, J. J., and S. PIERCE, 1963. Growth and physiology of Foraminifera in the laboratory: Part 4. Monoxenic culture of an allogromid with notes on its morphology. *J. Protozool.* **10**, 404–411.

LEE, J. J., S. PIERCE, S. H. HUTNER, B. J. SMITH and D. R. GURSKI, 1962. Trichomonads from poikilotherms: nutritional and physiological notes. *J. Protozool.* **9**, 445–450.

LEWIN, R. A., 1954. The utilization of acetate by wild type and mutant *Chlamydomonas dysmosos. J. Gen. Microbiol.* **11**, 459–471.

LYNCH, V. H. and M. CALVIN, 1953. $CO_2$ fixation by *Euglena. Ann. N. Y. Acad. Sci.* **56**, 890–900.

MCLAUGHLIN, J. J. A., 1958. Euryhaline chrysomonads: nutrition and toxigenesis in *Prymnesium parvum*, with notes on *Isochrysis galbana* and *Monochrysis lutheri. J. Protozool.* **5**, 75–81.

———— and P. A. ZAHL, 1959. Axenic zooxanthellae from various invertebrate hosts. *Ann. N. Y. Acad. Sci.* **77**, 55–72.

MCLAUGHLIN, J. J. A., P. A. ZAHL, A. NOWAK, J. MARCHISOTTO, and J. PRAGER, 1960. Mass cultivation of some phytoplanktons. *Ann. N. Y. Acad. Sci.* **90**, 856–865.

MAST, S. O., 1909. The reactions of *Didinium nasutum* with special reference to the feeding habits and the function of trichocysts. *Biol. Bull.* **16**, 91–118.

NATHAN, H. A., S. H. HUTNER, and H. L. LEVIN, 1958. Assay of pteridines with *Crithidia fasciculata. J. Protozool.* **5**, 134–138.

NEFF, R. J., 1957. Purification, axenic cultivation and description of a soil amoeba, *Acanthamoeba. J. Protozool.* **4**, 176–182.

NERO, L. C., M. G. TARVER, and R. L. HEDRICK, 1964. Growth of *Acanthamoeba castellani* with the yeast *Torulopsis famata. J. Bact.* **87**, 220–225.

NEWTON, B. A., 1957. Nutritional requirements and biosynthetic capabilities of the parasitic flagellate *Strigomonas oncopelti*. *J. Gen. Microbiol*. **17**, 708–717.

PENARD, E., 1905. Observations sur les amibes à pellicule. *Arch. f. Protistenk*. **6**, 175–206.

PROVASOLI, L., 1958. Nutrition and ecology of Protozoa and algae. *Ann. Rev. Microbiol*. **12**, 279–308.

———— 1958a. Growth factors in unicellular algae, in Buzatti-Traverso, A. A., *Perspectives in marine biology*, *Univ. Calif. Press*, Berkeley, 385–403.

———— and J. J. A., McLAUGHLIN, 1963. Limited heterotrophy of some photosynthetic dinoflagellates, C. H. OPPENHEIMER, ed., *Symposium on Marine Microbiology*, Springfield; Charles C Thomas, 105–113.

PROVASOLI, L., J. A. McLAUGHLIN, and M. R. DROOP, 1957. The development of artificial media for marine algae. Arch. f. Mikrobiol. 25: 392–428.

PROVASOLI, L., J. A. McLAUGHLIN, and I. J. PINTNER, 1954. Relative and limiting concentrations of major mineral constituents in the growth of algal flagellates. *Trans. N. Y. Acad. Sci*. **16**, 412–417.

PROVASOLI, L. and I. J. PINTNER, 1960. Artificial media for fresh-water algae, in C. A. TRYON and R. T. HARTMANN, *The ecology of algae*, *Pymatunning Symposia in Ecology*, University of Pittsburgh, 84–96.

SAGER, R., and S. GRANICK, 1953. Nutritional studies with *Chlamydomonas reinhardi*. *Ann. N. Y. Acad. Sci*. **56**, 831–838.

SANDON, H., 1932. The food of Protozoa. *Publ. Fac. Sci*. **No. 1**, Egyptian University, 197 pp.

SEAMAN, G. R., and R. M. REIFEL, 1963. Chemical composition and metabolism of Protozoa. *Ann. Rev. Microbiol*. **17**, 451–472.

SINGER, S., 1961. Some amino acid–folic interrelationships in *Tetrahymena pyriformis*. *J. Protozool*. **8**, 265–271.

SLATER, J. W., 1952. The influence of cobalt on the growth of the protozoan, *Tetrahymena*. *Physiol. Zool*. **25**, 323–332.

SUSSMAN, M., 1961. Cultivation and serial transfer of the slime mold, *Dictyostelium discoideum*, in a liquid medium. *J. Gen. Microbiol*. **25**, 375–378.

TANNREUTHER, G. W., 1923. Nutrition and reproduction in *Euglena*. *Arch. Entwickl., Orig*. **52**, 367–383.

TRAGER, W., 1957. Encystation of apostome ciliates in relation to molting of their crustacean hosts. *Biol. Bull*. **112**, 132–136.

———— 1957a. Nutrition of a haemoflagellate (*Leishmania tarentolae*) having an interchangeable requirement for choline or pyridoxal. *J. Protozool*. **4**, 269–276.

———— 1959. Tsetse-fly tissue culture and the development of trypanosomes to the infective stage. *Ann. Trop. Med. Parasitol*. **53**, 473–491.

———— and M. A. RUDZINSKA, 1964. The riboflavin requirement and the effects of acriflavin on the fine structure of the kinetoplast of *Leishmania tarentolae*. *J. Protozool*. **11**, 133–145.

VOGEL, H. J., 1959. Lysine biosynthesis in *Chlorella* and *Euglena*: phylogenetic significance. *Biochim. Biophys. Acta*. **34**, 282–283.

WAGTENDONK, W. J. VAN, 1955. The nutrition of ciliates, in S. H. HUTNER and A. LWOFF, *Biochemistry and Physiology of Protozoa*, Vol. 2. New York: Academic Press, 57–84.

WARNOCK, L. G., and J. VAN EYS, 1962. Normal carbohydrate metabolism in *Tetrahymena pyriformis*. *J. Cell. Comp. Physiol.* **60,** 53–60.

———— 1963. Inhibition of growth of *Tetrahymena pyriformis* by oxamic acid. *J. Bact.* **85,** 1179–1181.

WIESE, L., and R. F. JONES, 1963. Studies on gamete copulation in heterothallic chlamydomonads. *J. Cell. Comp. Physiol.* **61,** 265–274.

WILBUR, K. M., and N. WANATABE, 1963. Experimental studies on calcification in molluscs and the alga *Coccolithus huxleyi*. *Ann. N. Y. Acad. Sci.* **109,** 52–112.

WILLNER, E. N., 1956. Factors which influence the acquisition of flagella by the amoeba, *Naegleria gruberi*. *J. Exp. Biol.* **33,** 583–603.

WILSON, B. W., and W. F. DANFORTH, 1958. The extent of acetate and ethanol oxidation by *Euglena gracilis*. *J. Gen. Microbiol.* **18,** 535–542.

WISE, D., 1959. Carbon nutrition and metabolism of *Polytomella caeca*. *J. Protozool.* **6,** 19–23.

————, W. COOL, J. MARSH, V. KEARNS-PRESTON, F. MUELLER, and T. M. LIDDLE, 1961. Alcohol nutrition of an acetate flagellate. *J. Protozool.* **8,** Suppl.: 8.

WU, C., and J. F. HOGG, 1952. The amino acid composition and nitrogen metabolism of *Tetrahymena geleii*. *J. Biol. Chem.* **198,** 753–764.

# 4. Protozoan Nutrition in Applied Protozoology

## Protozoa as Assay Organisms

The application of Protozoa to bioassay techniques was a logical extension of earlier microbiological procedures. Such applications had to wait, of course, for the identification of protozoan food requirements in axenic culture media of known chemical composition. In theory, the procedure is simple enough once chemically defined media and organisms with known requirements are available. Unfortunately, things are not quite so simple as they might seem at first. The ideal culture medium for an assay organism would be so constructed that growth could be stimulated only by addition of the substance to be estimated. Without this test substance, growth in the basal medium should approach zero. Furthermore, the stimulation of growth would be proportional to the added factor within a practical range of concentrations. In the presence of a maximal concentration of the substance being assayed the organism would reproduce at the maximal rate possible for the conditions of incubation. With such a medium, nutritious materials likely to be encountered in the assay of natural products would have no significant sparing action on a particular growth factor or other required substance. A different practical hazard in bioassays of natural materials is the possibility that something in the sample may retard growth of the assay organism to a measurable extent and so lead to inaccurate assays. Averting any such effect in advance is probably impossible because a clue to the identity of the inhibitor would be a prerequisite for preventing or reversing its action. Hence, modification of an assay to fit particular types of materials might even be necessary in special cases.

Development of a medium approaching the ideal type may require repeated testing under practical conditions. The important practical problems and potential applications have been outlined in some detail, with appropriate recommendations where possible (Hutner, Cury, and Baker, 1958; Hutner, Provasoli and Baker, 1961). Once developed to the stage of practical utility, such an assay medium can be a very useful analytical asset. The actual practical value depends upon several factors, such as the sensitivity and specificity of the assay organism for a particular growth factor or essential nutrient, the time required for completing the test, and the cost in time and energy expended in preparing assay media and carrying out the rest of the procedure. Certain of the attempted protozoological assays have passed such practical tests and are being used in clinical and other laboratories.

### VITAMIN $B_{12}$

One of the best known of these procedures is the assay of vitamin $B_{12}$, for which two Protozoa have been used — *Euglena gracilis*, preferably strain *z* (Hutner, Bach and Ross, 1956), and *Ochromonas malhamensis* (Ford, 1953; Hutner, *et al.*, 1957, 1960). In some respects, *Ochromonas* is more satisfactory because it grows rapidly and shows a response similar to that of mammals, whereas *E. gracilis* reacts also to analogues which are inactive in higher animals. However, *E. gracilis* is very sensitive, responding to concentrations as low as 0.25 $\mu\mu g/ml$. Results obtained with the *Euglena* assay would provide an estimate of "total $B_{12}$ activity" while the *Ochromonas* assay yields a more restricted estimate, that of the $B_{12}$ factors active for mammals and birds. The *Ochromonas* assay is an official microbiological procedure in Great Britain.

These $B_{12}$ assays have been applied to such clinical matters as tracing the urinary excretion of $B_{12}$ in patients with various disorders of the liver (Baker, *et al.*, 1958), comparing the plasma level and blood cell content of $B_{12}$ in pernicious anemia patients especially, and in estimating the $B_{12}$ content of cerebrospinal fluid in patients with disorders of the central nervous system. In ecological investigations, protozoological assays have been used for estimating the $B_{12}$ content of pond waters, seawater samples from near shore and from the open ocean, and also of mud deposited near the mouths of rivers. Recent observations (Gold, 1964) on responses of a marine dinoflagellate to vitamin $B_{12}$ indicate that it may be possible to assay enriched seawater directly within a period of about 24 hours, measuring assimilation of $C^{14}$ instead of population growth.

### THIAMINE

In addition to service in the bioassay of vitamin $B_{12}$, *Ochromonas malhamensis* is useful as an assay organism for thiamine (Baker, *et al.*, 1959). As such, it is particularly suitable because, unlike some phyto-flagellates, it requires intact thiamine instead of the thiazole or both thiazole and pyrimidine moieties. The specificity and sensitivity of the technique make it useful for assaying thiamine in blood, cerebrospinal fluid and urine. For example, the assay has been applied to a comparison of fetal and maternal vitamin levels at parturition, the data indicating that the fetal circulation accumulates thiamine at the expense of maternal supplies and even to the dangerous depletion of maternal reserves. A preliminary digestion, preferably enzymatic (phosphatase), is necessary because *O. malhamensis* has no enzyme for releasing bound thiamine. Results of the *Ochromonas* assay have shown good agreement with other and less convenient techniques.

### BIOTIN

The assay of biotin with *Ochromonas danica* (Baker, *et al.*, 1962) is a sensitive technique which has been tested with whole blood, brain tissue, liver, serum and urine. Except for urine, which contains free biotin, such natural materials have been subjected to preliminary digestion with papain in order to release bound biotin.

## NICOTINIC ACID

*Tetrahymena pyriformis* has been applied to the assay of nicotinic acid (Baker, *et al.*, 1960). This method is reliable over a wide range of concentrations (about 1-300 m$\mu$g/ml, as compared with a much lower maximum in the usual *Lactobacillus* assay), and the requirements of *T. pyriformis* seem to parallel those of higher animals for nicotinic acid. The *Tetrahymena* assay has been used with samples of blood, serum and urine and is quite specific and sensitive with such biological materials.

## PANTOTHENIC ACID

*T. pyriformis* has also served in the assay of pantothenic acid in body fluids (Baker, *et al.*, 1960) and, as an outgrowth of preliminary findings, in a comparison of pantothenate levels in maternal and fetal blood at birth. Just as in the case of thiamine, the pantothenate levels were much higher in fetal blood samples.

## THIOCTIC ACID

The assay of thioctic acid also has been carried out with *T. pyriformis* (Stokstad, *et al.*, 1956), the first protozoon shown to need this growth factor.

## PTERIDINES

*Crithidia fasciculata* is serving in the assay of pteridines (Nathan, *et al.*, 1958). These substances, as a group, are rather widely distributed. Among other locations, such as the eyes of *Drosophila*, several different pteridines occur in the skin of a number of amphibian species in the inclusions of pigment cells (chromatophores). Biopterin occurs in amphibian skin in lower concentrations than some of the other and more highly colored pteridines. *C. fasciculata* is the one protozoon, so far reported, which requires an unconjugated pteridine, biopterin being the most active. This factor stimulates growth of *C. fasciculata* in concentrations as low as 0.03 m$\mu$g/ml.

## Protozoa as Experimental Animals

Protozoa in axenic cultures have now been used in a wide variety of investigations as experimental animals. There is already a certain amount of latitude in the choice of organisms and it is sometimes possible to select species with particularly desirable combinations of traits. Of course, there are still many untamed species with very interesting attributes, so that continued attempts at domestication are to be expected. A number of the presently available "useful" organisms have participated in interesting biochemical research. Toward the more practical pharmacological side, various others have served in research bearing more or less directly on rather practical matters. Even protozoologists are sometimes a bit surprised by protozoan versatility.

Among the applications aimed at answering questions of general biochemical interest, axenic cultures have sometimes supplied material for analysis — for example, the chromatographic analysis of *Tetrahymena pyriformis* for estimation of free and bound amino acids in these ciliates; comparative analysis of different strains of *T. pyriformis* in a search for consistent chemical differences; comparing the specific protein contents of different strains of *Amoeba;* tracing amino acid content in relation to different phases of growth and fission; identification of fatty acids in *Ochromonas danica* grown in a defined medium. In another general type of investigations, axenic cultures have been used to trace certain aspects of metabolism — identification of the essential amino acids which *Tetrahymena* uses in the synthesis of non-essential amino acids omitted from the culture medium; utilization of $C^{14}$-labeled amino acids by *Crithidia oncopelti* in synthesis of other amino acids; utilization of $C^{14}$-labeled substrates (glucose, acetate, amino acids, purines, pyrimidines) in synthesis of certain amino acids and nucleic acid components; similarly, using $C^{14}$-glucose for comparing glucose metabolism in different strains of a pathogenic trypanosome; confirming the intracellular formation of coccoliths in a species of *Hymenomonas* by adding $Ca^{45}$ to axenic cultures; tracing catabolism of particular amino acids by *T. pyriformis;* using *T. pyriformis* in a search for clues to the mechanism underlying the Pasteur effect; tracing the uptake of radioactive minerals and labeled vitamins in *T. pyriformis;* tracing sulfate-$S^{35}$ into the amino acid metabolism of *Euglena;* tracing radioactive thymidine into DNA in *T. pyriformis;*

estimating growth of a photosynthetic dinoflagellate by measuring uptake of radioactive carbon (supplied as $NaHC^{14}CO_3$); tracing the relation between rate of glucose utilization and age of the culture in *T. pyriformis;* analysis of isolated cilia of *T. pyriformis* for various physical and chemical properties; analysis of the "chromatin body" extruded from the macronucleus during division in *T. rostrata;* attempting to identify the disabilities of a chlorophyll-bearing flagellate which cannot grow in darkness, although motility is retained for several days; isolation and characterization of DNA from different species of Protozoa; using electrophoretic techniques for separating proteins and localizing specific enzyme activity; differentiation of serological types in *Tetrahymena;* a comparison of the types of fatty acids found in normally green and in bleached strains of *Euglena gracilis;* identification of biochemical mutants in *Chlamydomonas* and *Tetrahymena* and tracing the inheritance of specific growth requirements. Attempts to suppress the inhibitory action of urethan on *Poteriochromonas* resulted in a suggestion that glumatic acid is probably a precursor of thymine in this flagellate.

More immediately practical applications, often pharmacological in nature, are already common (Hutner, 1964). As test organisms for detecting and interpreting mechanisms of drug toxicity at the cellular level, possible applications are numerous. One advantage of such test organisms is that some of them are distinctly animal-like in metabolism, often resembling man and some of the other higher animals in certain specific requirements. The potential utility of such species is augmented, of course, if their susceptibility to a particular drug is more or less comparable to that of higher animals. And then there is one important practical advantage in using Protozoa as test animals: they are less of a strain on the laboratory budget than the commonly used laboratory mammals and birds. In addition, experimental results are usually obtained rather quickly. A few sample investigations are mentioned below.

In trying to determine specific effects of one of the tranquilizers, chlorpromazine, it was found that *Tetrahymena pyriformis* was affected primarily through an increase in permeability of the body wall (Nathan and Friedman, 1962). This type of change permitted entry of certain substances much more rapidly than in the normal organism. For example, histidine, an amino acid required by *T. pyriformis*, became inhibitory when the concentration in the culture medium was increased beyond a certain minimum. Excessive uptake of the amino acid, which is a good metal chelator, presumably interfered with metabolism by binding too much of the endogenous supply of trace metals. As was expected in such a case, the inhibition was relieved by adding a metal (such as calcium, iron, magnesium or zinc) to the medium.

Some of the antihistamines have been tested on several flagellates (*Chlamydomonas, Chlorogonium, Euglena, Ochromonas*) and on *Tetrahymena pyriformis*. Inhibitory effects on growth could be annuled in several cases by histidine, but not by histamine, indicating significant interference with amino acid metabolism involving histidine (Sanders and Nathan, 1959).

Two tumor-inhibiting compounds, both cyclic amino acids, have been tested on *Ochromonas danica*, using several natural amino acids as possible reversing agents. The effect of one of the inhibitors was reversed by L-alanine and, much less extensively, by glycine. Effects of the other cyclopentane were reversed by L-leucine, the results in the two cases suggesting that at the cellular level these drugs interfere with synthesis of particular amino acids (Aaronson and Bensky, 1962).

The "cellular" effects of urethan, which has been used for relief of certain leukemias, have been investigated with another chrysomonad, *Poteriochromonas stipitata*. Growth was stimulated by low concentrations of the drug, but inhibited at higher concentrations (0.1–0.3% w/v). This inhibition was prevented by thymine and some of its supposed precursors.

Tests of thalidomide on *Tetrahymena* and several flagellates indicated that, at the cellular level, this somewhat notorious drug interferes with oxidative mechanisms in which nicotinamide is involved.

The reversal of inhibition, by the "*Crithidia*" factor and folic acid, of an anticonvulsant drug (Primidone) on *Crithidia fasciculata* and *Escherichia coli* suggested that action of the drug involves primarily an interference with the folic-catalyzed synthesis of pyrimidines. Such effects obviously could be related to the known involvement of such anticonvulsants in the appearance of anemias in man (Baker, *et al.*, 1962).

*Crithidia fasciculata* also has been tried in the evaluation of potential antimalarial drugs of the anti-folic type, Daraprim being used as a standard for comparison (Nathan and Cowperthwaite, 1954). The results on *Crithidia*, measured as inhibition of growth, agreed rather well with known effects on malarial parasites *in vivo*.

One of the herbicides (3-amino-1, 2, 4-triazole) has been tested on *Euglena gracilis, Ochromonas* spp., a bacterium, and a small plant,

*Spirodela.* Temporary bleaching of the green forms resulted and reproduction of the flagellates was inhibited (Aaronson and Scher, 1960), as
was growth of *Spirodela.* Also, catalase activity in *Ochromonas* was
inhibited by fairly high concentrations of the drug, supposedly by interference with synthesis of heme-containing enzymes through chelation
of iron (Aaronson, 1960).

One of the more unusual tasks assigned to Protozoa has been that
of estimating the relative toxicity of radiopaque agents currently used
in angiography. The effects on *Tetrahymena pyriformis*, read in terms of
reduced motility, showed good correlation with observations on toxicity
of the same materials in higher animals (Mark, *et al.*, 1963).

## Bibliography

AARONSON, S., 1960. Mode of action of 3-amino-1, 2, 4-triazole on photosynthetic microorganisms. *J. Protozool.* **7,** 289–294.

————— and B. BENSKY 1962. Study of the cellular action of drugs with
Protozoa. I. Effect of 1-1-amino*cyclo*pentane-1-carboxylic acid and 1-amino-
3-methyl*cyclo*hexane-1-carboxylic acid on the phytoflagellate *Ochromonas
danica. Biochem. Pharmacol.* **11,** 983–986.

AARONSON, S., and S. SCHER 1960. Effect of aminotriazole and streptomycin
on multiplication and pigment production of photosynthetic microorganisms.
*J. Protozool.* **7,** 156–158.

BAKER, H., G. BRILL, I. PASHER and H. SOBOTKA, 1958. Vitamin $B_{12}$ excretion
as index of hepatic disorders. II. Correlation with liver-function tests. *Clin.
Chem.* **4,** 27–31.

—————, O. FRANK, S. H. HUTNER, S. AARONSON, H. ZIFFER, and H. SOBOTKA,
1962. Lesions in folic acid metabolism induced by Primidone. *Experientia*
**18,** 224–229.

BAKER, H., O. FRANK, V. B. MATOVITCH, I. PASHER, S. AARONSON, S. H. HUTNER,
and H. SOBOTKA, 1962. A new assay method for biotin in blood, serum, urine,
and tissues. *Anal. Biochem.* **3,** 31–39.

BAKER, H., O. FRANK, I. PASHER, A. DINNERSTEIN, and H. SOBOTKA, 1960.
An assay for pantothenic acid in biologic fluids. *Clinical Chem.* **6,** 35–42.

BAKER, H., O. FRANK, I. PASHER, S. H. HUTNER, and H. SOBOTKA, 1960.
Nicotinic acid assay in blood and urine. *Clinical Chem.* **6,** 572–577.

BAKER, H., O. FRANK, I. PASHER, and H. SOBOTKA, 1960. Vitamin $B_{12}$ in human
blood and serum. I. Comparison of microbiological assays using normal
subjects. *Clinical Chem.* **6,** 578–581.

BAKER, H., O. FRANK, I. PASHER, H. ZIFFER, and H. SOBOTKA, 1960. Pantothenic
acid, thiamine and folic acid levels at parturition. *Proc. Soc. Exper. Med.*
**103,** 321–323.

BAKER, H., I. PASHER, O. FRANK, S. H. HUTNER, S. AARONSON, and H. SOBOTKA, 1959. Assay of thiamine in biological fluids. *Clinical Chem.* **5,** 13–17.

FORD, J. E., 1953. The microbiological assay of vitamin $B_{12}$. The specificity of the requirement of *Ochromonas malhamensis* for cyanocobalamin. *Brit. J. Nutrition* **7,** 299–306.

GOLD, K., 1964. Aspects of marine dinoflagellate nutrition measured by $C^{14}$ assimilation. *J. Protozool.* **11,** 85–89.

HUTNER, S. H., 1964. Protozoa as toxicological tools. *J. Protozool.* **11,** 1–6.

HUTNER, S. H., M. K. BACH, and G. I. M. ROSS, 1956. A sugar-containing basal medium for vitamin $B_{12}$-assay with *Euglena;* application to body fluids. *J. Protozool.* **3,** 101–112.

HUTNER, S. H., H. BAKER, S. AARONSON, H. A. NATHAN, E. RODRIGUEZ, S. LOCKWOOD, M. SANDERS, and R. A. PETERSEN, 1957. Growing *Ochromonas malhamensis* above 35°. *J. Protozool.* **4,** 259–269.

HUTNER, S. H., A. CURY, and H. BAKER, 1958. Microbiological assays. *Anal. Chem.* **30,** 849–867.

HUTNER, S. H., L. PROVASOLI, and H. BAKER, 1961. Development of microbiological assays for biochemical, oceanographic, and clinical use. *Microchem. J., Symposium Ser.* **1,** 95–113.

MARK, M. F., A. M. IMPARATO, S. H. HUTNER, and H. BAKER, 1963. Estimate of toxicity of radiopaque agents by means of a ciliate. *Angiology* **14,** 383–389.

NATHAN, H. A., and J. COWPERTHWAITE, 1954. Use of the trypanosomid flagellate, *Crithidia fasciculata*, for evaluating antimalarials. *Proc. Soc. Exp. Biol. Med.* **85,** 117–119.

NATHAN, H. A., and W. FRIEDMAN, 1962. Chlorpromazine affects permeability of resting cells of *Tetrahymena pyriformis*. *Science* **135,** 793–794.

NATHAN, H. A., S. H. HUTNER, and H. L. LEVIN, 1958. Assay of pteridines with *Crithidia fasciculata*. *J. Protozool.* **5,** 134–138.

SANDERS, M., and H. A. NATHAN, 1959. Protozoa as pharmacological tools: the antihistamines. *J. Gen Microbiol.* **21,** 264–270.

STOKSTAD, E. L. R., G. R. SEAMAN, R. J. DAVIS, and S. H. HUTNER, 1956. Assay of thioctic acid, in Glick, D., *Methods in Biochemical Analysis*, v. 3, New York: Interscience Publishers, pp. 23–47.

# INDEX

# Index

ABCDEFGHIJ   0698765

ABOUT THE AUTHOR


Richard P. Hall has been Professor of Biology at New York University since 1938. He was President of the Society of Protozoologists from 1949 to 1951 and President of the American Microscopical Society in 1957. Professor Hall is a fellow of the American Association for the Advancement of Science and of the New York Academy of Sciences. He is a member of the American Society of Naturalists, the American Institute of Biological Sciences, the American Society of Parasitologists, the American Society of Tropical Medicine and Hygiene, the American Society of Zoologists, and the Society for Experimental Biology and Medicine. He writes occasional articles in biological journals and is the author of *Protozoa*, published in the United States and — in a modern Asia edition — in Tokyo.

THIS BOOK WAS SET IN

TIMES ROMAN AND DEEPDENE TYPES

BY TRADE COMPOSITION, INC.

IT WAS DESIGNED BY THE STAFF OF

BLAISDELL PUBLISHING COMPANY.